Guide to

MW05

Minor Works Building Contract (MW)

Minor Works Building Contract With
Contractor's Design (MWD)

RIBA ✱ **Publishing**   **Sarah Lupton**

© Sarah Lupton, 2007

Published by RIBA Publishing,
15 Bonhill Street, London EC2P 2EA

ISBN 978 1 85946 247 8

Stock code 58500

British Library Cataloguing in Publications Data
A catalogue record for this book is available from the British Library.

Publisher: Steven Cross
Commissioning Editor: Matthew Thompson
Project Editor: Anna Walters
Editor: David Hawthorn
Designed by Casciani Evans Wood
Typeset by Academic + Technical Typesetting, Bristol
Printed and bound by MPG Books, Cornwall

Guide to

MW05

Foreword

The Minor Building Works Contract is by far the most widely used standard form of building contract and plays a vitally important part in the procurement of small scale building projects. The 2005 edition of the Minor Building Works Contract comes in two versions, one that includes provision for the contractor to carry out some of the design, and one that does not. While this new edition enjoys a more logical layout, a clearer format, and even greater simplification, its attractive brevity means it is inevitably more dependent upon implied terms than some other JCT contracts. For example, the procedural rules are minimal for those unfamiliar with contract administration and law and this may raise questions for which answers are sought.

Fortunately, Sarah Lupton's new *Guide to MW05*, which follows on from her excellent *Guide to MW98*, offers comprehensive guidance and does so in language that is easily understood. Organised by themes, the book is a straightforward analysis of the contract in the light of today's legal and practice landscape, referring to recent case law and clearly distinguishing that guidance which applies only to the *with contractor's design* version. The hard-pressed practitioner also will find the Guide helpful as it outlines the changes from the 1998 edition. Practitioners will be particularly pleased to see the useful indexes and clause comparison table, and will doubtless come to depend on being able to dip quickly into the book for specific help during the course of a project.

I would thoroughly recommend the book to both architecture and other construction students on the threshold of undertaking their professional examinations. The comprehensive up-to-date coverage clearly and succinctly exposes the legal ramifications of the contract. Sarah Lupton's rare combination of being a legally-trained architect who also runs the MA in Professional Studies at Cardiff University makes this book the ideal student companion.

Professor Peter Hibberd
Secretary-General, The Joint Contracts Tribunal
February 2007

Contents

About the Guide

This is the second edition of the book originally entitled *Guide to MW98*, published in 1999. The subject of that book was the *JCT Agreement for Minor Building Works*, which is now called the *Minor Works Building Contract* (MW05). Since it was first published, this form has been an extremely popular choice for smaller projects, and is likely to continue to be so, particularly now that there is also a version (MWD05) for use where the contractor is to design a part of the works.

The guide is intended to be a practical aid for busy practitioners and students who need to understand the operation and administration of MW05 and MWD05. It explains the provisions of the contract and how they might work in practice. It does not assume any prior knowledge of the form. As its provisions are relatively brief, contracts let on the form may be subject to implied terms, and the guide includes a short introduction to this area of contract law.

The commentary includes a broad outline of the form and the reasons why it might be selected. It describes the various documents that may form part of the contract package at the time it is entered into. It examines the Contractor's obligations with respect to quality and standard of work, including the design obligations under MWD05. Matters of programming and extensions of time are also dealt with, as well as the powers of the administrator to monitor and control the standard of work. It analyses the procedures for adjusting the contract sum and the process of certification, and deals with matters of insurance, termination and dispute resolution. Finally, it covers the changes introduced by Amendment 1 to the form, which include adjustments to deal with the CDM Regulations 2007 and the new clause 5.4C provision for insurance of the works.

The author would like to thank Lucy Murawski for her invaluable help in preparing the clause comparison tables, checking the text, and for providing Figure 7.

1 About MW05

1.1 There are two versions of the Minor Works Building Contract 2005, one that includes provision for the contractor to carry out design (the 'Minor Works Building Contract with contractor's design', MWD05) and one that does not (MW05). Apart from the provisions relating to design, the two versions are otherwise identical. Therefore, although this guide refers to MW05 throughout, the points made are equally applicable to both versions. Where matters relating to MWD05 only are covered, these are clearly distinguished.

1.2 Both versions can be used by both private clients and local authorities. There is, in addition, a variant of the earlier MW98 form still in print, which was prepared for use in renovation grant work carried out under the Local Government and Housing Act 1989. This is entitled the Agreement for Housing Grant Works (HG(A)), for use with an architect/contract administrator. It is currently published in a 2002 edition, although it is understood that it is to be updated in line with MW05, and republished in 2008 under the title 'Housing Grant Works Building Contract' (HG).

1.3 Separate editions of MW05 and MWD05 are published jointly with the SBCC for use in Scotland. The key differences are the absence of the attestation, the inclusion of provisions for bills of quantities, an additional Schedule for listing the Contract Documents, and detailed guidance on 'signing' under Scottish law.

1.4 There are no separate supplements published for use with MW05. Provisions concerning arbitration and fluctuations are included as Schedules 1 and 2 at the back of the form. The form also includes a Guidance Note. The generic JCT short form of sub-contract would be suitable for use alongside MW05, although MW05 does not require this.

Key features

1.5 MW05 is a traditional lump sum contract, relatively simple in its overall structure and with few procedural rules. The contractor undertakes to carry out the work shown in the Contract Documents identified in the first recital, by the completion date entered in the Contract Particulars, in return for a Contract Sum entered in Article 2. There are provisions for varying the work, together with mechanisms for adjusting the Contract Sum and the completion date. In general terms, the contract assumes that all work is designed by the contract administrator. Under the MWD05 version there is provision whereby design responsibility can be assigned to the contractor for an identified part or parts of the works (termed the Contractor's Designed Portion). Apart from this provision, the forms assume that the contractor will have no design role.

1.6 The form requires the appointment of an 'Architect/Contract Administrator', who is responsible for issuing all further information necessary for the carrying out of the Works.

At some points the contract administrator is acting as the employer's agent, and at others as an independent administrator. A court would assume that the parties have contracted on the basis that the contract administrator will act fairly at all times in applying the terms of the contract and particularly so when deciding such matters as payments due to the contractor, and extensions of time. This duty of fairness, however, does not place the contract administrator in the same position as an arbitrator, in that the contract administrator is not immune from being sued.

1.7   The contractor takes full responsibility for ensuring that the standards set out in the Contract Documents are achieved, and this includes direct responsibility for any sub-contracted work. The form provides for domestic sub-contractors chosen by the contractor subject to the written consent of the contract administrator. There is no provision by which the contractor can be required to use a sub-contractor named or nominated by the contract administrator.

1.8   The work to be undertaken will be in accordance with the Contract Documents, but will also include varied or additional work subsequently instructed as provided for in the Conditions. The Contract Sum may be adjusted and is qualified by the wording 'or such other sum as shall become payable under this Contract' (Article 2). The amount of work which is covered by the Contract Sum should be described in exact terms in the Contract Documents. The work is described in drawings, and/or a specification and/or schedules of work and, where the Contractor's Designed Portion is used, the employer must state its requirements for the design of that part (the Employer's Requirements). The contractor prices the specification or work schedules or provides a schedule of rates. Generally, if the description is inaccurate, any resulting addition to the cost is borne by the employer. If the contractor has made an error in pricing, however, then any shortfall will be borne by the contractor. The contract administrator has wide powers to order variations to the Works if required, and the contractor has a corresponding right to be paid any additional costs that arise from such variations.

1.9   Progress payments are made to the contractor every four weeks following the issue of contract administrator's certificates. In general terms, the certificates will reflect the amount of work that has been properly completed up to the point of valuation in accordance with the terms of the contract. None of these certificates are conclusive evidence that the contractor has fulfilled its obligations under the contract. There is no reference to the appointment of a quantity surveyor, and there are no functions assigned to such a person in the Conditions. The contract administrator therefore has a significant role, which extends to the valuation of variations, the valuation of work executed, and the computation of the final sum due. Unusually, if agreement on the cost of variations is required before the work is carried out, this agreement is a matter between the contractor and the contract administrator. If a quantity surveyor is appointed by the employer, he or she would act solely as adviser to the contract administrator and employer, and would have no active role under the form.

1.10   The form complies with requirements of the Housing Grants, Construction and Regeneration Act 1996 (HGCRA 1996), and therefore includes provisions relating to withholding notices, suspension and adjudication, which that Act requires in all construction contracts to which

Figure 1 The HGCRA 1996 provisions

HGCRA 1996	MW05 clause	Provision concerning
S108	Cl 7·2	Adjudication
S109	Cl 4·3	Stage payments
S110	Cl 4·3/4·8·3	Dates for payment
S111	Cl 4·8·1/4·8	Notices
S112	Cl 4·7	Contractor's right of suspension
S115	Cl 1·6	Notices

it applies. A notable exclusion is contracts where one of the parties is the residential occupier of the property on which the work is to be carried out. In practice many projects which fall within this exception may be tendered on MW05, and for those projects the clauses are not required. Though the statutory clauses were identified in Amendment 11 to MW80, which first introduced the provisions, they are not identified in MW05. As the difference is significant, this guide indicates throughout those provisions that result from the requirements of the Act (*see* Figure 1).

Changes since MW98

1.11   The most obvious changes to the form relate to its appearance, layout and style. The new form is more attractive and modern in appearance, and the layout and numbering have been clarified for ease of use. The form used to require insertions at various points in the clauses; these have now been grouped together at the start under a 'Contract Particulars' section in line with other JCT contracts, which helps to ensure that nothing is overlooked when completing the form. Care should be taken when completing the Articles and the Contract Particulars, as many of the defaults have changed, for example if nothing is inserted in Article 5 the contract administrator will be the Planning Supervisor. The CIS provisions and the VAT supplementary agreement have been removed, as these are matters of statute rather than contract. The most significant change is, of course, the addition of the version with contractor design, as discussed throughout this guide. Users should also note the changes to the dispute resolution provisions, i.e. that litigation not arbitration is now the default option, and that adjudication will be conducted under the rules of the Scheme for Construction Contracts. A list of key changes is set out in Figure 2.

Deciding on MW05

1.12   A headnote at the front of the form states that it is appropriate for work that is simple in character, where the work is designed by or on behalf of the employer, and for where a contract administrator has been appointed to administer the conditions. The Guidance Note included at the back of the form adds that it is intended for where a lump sum offer has been obtained at tender stage, based on documents sufficiently detailed for the .

Figure 2 Key changes

Layout/terminology differences:
- Contract Particulars now included.
- Default entries in Articles and Contract Particulars revised.
- New provision for execution as a deed.
- Definitions clause included.
- New defined terms, e.g. 'Date for Commencement of the Works' and 'Rectification Period'.
- 'Architect' now 'Architect/contract administrator'.
- 'Determination' now 'termination'.

Omissions:
- Construction Industry Scheme provisions largely removed.
- VAT supplementary agreement removed.

Additions:
- New version with Contractor's Designed Portion provisions.
- Contractor to encourage employees etc to register under the CSCS.
- Contract administrator and contractor required to 'endeavour to agree' the cost of variations.
- Contract administrator required to notify contractor of defects in rectification period.
- Provision for termination due to corruption.
- Provision for termination due to suspension for neutral events.

Other changes:
- Arbitration – default changed to legal proceedings.
- Adjudication – now under the Scheme.
- Mediation – moved from footnote to an express clause.

---

contractor to be able to price accurately without a Bill of Quantities. The anticipated contract period should be such that full fluctuations provisions are not required (in practice it would be appropriate for programmes up to 12 months). JCT Practice Note 5 (series 2) stated that MW98 was 'suitable for contracts up to the value of £100,000 (2001 prices)', but the 2006 version of this Note 'Deciding on the appropriate JCT contract' does not set out any limits. It is generally recognised that it is the nature of the project, rather than its value, that should be the deciding factor, and that the form can be used successfully on larger projects provided they are straightforward.

1.13   In the case of MWD05, the headnote adds that the this version is suitable for projects where the contractor is required to design discrete part(s), and the employer has had detailed requirements prepared for that design. The headnote makes it clear that the form is not suitable for use as a design and build contract, in such cases the JCT Design and Build Contract would be the appropriate choice.

1.14   One of the most striking characteristics about MW05 is its brevity, at least in comparison with most other standard forms. Its popularity suggests that this apparent advantage is appealing to many. However, the fact that the contract is silent on many matters can create problems. The procedural rules are minimal, and there is little precise information on the content, form and timing of notices, etc, leaving the parties to agree their own in advance or to sort matters out as they proceed. The contract is also silent on the rights of the parties should certain circumstances arise, many of them quite common in practice. This will not mean that the parties have no rights, as in many cases the courts would imply a term into a contract to cover the particular situation.

1.15   Somewhat paradoxically with MW05 there is a greater need to understand the general principles of contract law, in particular the law relating to implied terms, than there is with forms of contract which are longer and more sophisticated. Unfortunately, this fact is sometimes not appreciated, and there have been notorious cases of architects mishandling administration under the Agreement for Minor Building Works, often through failing to understand the legal framework in which it operates. This chapter includes a short summary of the principles of implied terms, which are referred to at several points in the guide. However, if complex issues arise the contract administrator should be prepared to take legal advice.

1.16   Before advising on whether or not to use MW05, the contract administrator needs to be as aware of what is missing as of what is included, and to consider whether the absence of matters not expressly included might cause difficulties. For example, is it important to use certain sub-contractors or suppliers, or will there be a design element in some specialist sub-contract work which should be covered by a warranty, or does the employer intend to remain in occupation throughout the work, thereby involving the contractor in some decanting and phased programming of the Works?

1.17   If the Contractor's Designed Portion is to be used, it should be noted that there is no provision for requiring Professional Indemnity Insurance from the contractor. The procedures for the contractor to submit the developing design are limited, for example the interval between submission of information and starting the relevant work may be as little as seven days, and there is no system by which the contract administrator may comment or require changes. If such procedures are required, the employer should be advised to consider the CDP provisions in ICD05. Some of the key missing items to be aware of in selecting MW05 and MWD05 are set out in Figure 3.

1.18   It is often the case that minor building work will be commissioned by less experienced clients for 'once in a lifetime' operations. Although the amounts of money involved may be relatively small, to many employers they are a very significant expenditure. Despite this context, in some areas the contract is less protective of the employer than one might expect. For example, although the SBC requirements for a right to interest in sub-contracts (protecting the sub-contractor) has been stepped down into MW05, the sub-contract conditions designed to protect the employer in regard to ownership of unfixed materials have not. It is therefore important for the contract administrator to take time and care to explain to the client the respective obligations of the parties, particularly in respect of matters such as insurance and payment of sums properly due. Whilst such matters as extensions of time and reimbursement of loss and expense are covered in the form, the procedures are somewhat slight. The employer may therefore be unaware at the time of

Figure 3 Key provisions not included in MW05

- a clerk of works.
- phased possession or completion.
- use or occupation of the site by the employer during the Works.
- nominated or named sub-contractors or suppliers.
- the contractor to notify the contract administrator of discrepancies between the Contract Documents.
- the contractor to notify the contract administrator of delays, unless the delay will result in late completion and unless caused by reasons beyond the contractor's control.
- the employer to employ others direct, or the contractor to allow access for directly engaged workmen.
- the contract administrator to reduce the contract period if work omitted.
- the contract administrator to award an extension of time without a notice from the contractor.
- the contract administrator to extend the contract period for delaying events occurring after the date for completion has passed.
- the contract administrator to review extensions of time previously given.
- the contract administrator to award loss and/or expense, unless resulting from a variation.
- the contract administrator to require work to be opened up, tested or removed.
- the contract administrator to make deductions from the Contract Sum if defective work is to remain.
- the contract administrator to visit the contractor's or sub-contractors' workshops.
- the contractor to include 'property vesting' clauses in all sub-contracts.
- CDP PII insurance requirements.
- CDP design submission procedure.
- copyright in the Contractor's Design Documents.
- provisions for collateral warranties from the contractor or any sub-contractor.

any delays in progress, as MW05 does not require the contractor to notify the contract administrator until it becomes apparent that completion will not be achieved. Even then it seems that this operates only when the delay is due to reasons 'beyond the control' of the contractor.

1.19   For larger or more complex projects, IC05 or ICD05, which contain all the provisions listed in Figure 3, may therefore be a more appropriate choice (see also Figure 4). For smaller projects, particularly those for domestic work, the clear and simple contracts for Home Owner/Occupier (HOO) may be used. These do not contain the Housing Grants Act provisions, as discussed above (as they are not required on projects where the employer is a residential occupier) but they also have significant further limitations, for example there are no liquidated damages provisions. For very small repair jobs, the Repair and Maintenance Contracts could be used, with one version for domestic and one for commercial work.

1.20   In many cases, however, MW05 or MWD05 will be an entirely appropriate selection, and the form justifies its popularity. It is simple to complete, easy to refer to, and generally much less daunting to the less experienced client or builder than most other building contract forms. It is of course possible to introduce amendments to tailor the form to particular situations, but this should not be done without legal advice. If major changes are needed then a more appropriate form of contract should be considered. Otherwise

Figure 4 Comparison of standard forms

	ICD	IC	MWD	MW	HOO
Contractor design	yes		yes		
'Contractor's Design Submission Procedure'					
Possession by sections	yes	yes			
Completion by sections	yes	yes			
Deferment of possession	yes	yes			
Information release schedule	yes	yes			
Partial possession	yes	yes			
Clerk of works	yes	yes			
Named sub-contractors/specialists	yes	yes			
Advance payment, bond	yes	yes			
Activity schedule	yes	yes			
Payment for off-site materials, bond	yes	yes			
Interest on late payment	yes	yes	yes	yes	
Professional Indemnity Insurance	yes				
Joint Fire Code	yes	yes			
Mediation	yes	yes	yes	yes	
Adjudication	yes	yes	yes	yes	yes
Arbitration	yes	yes	yes	yes	
Litigation	yes	yes	yes	yes	yes
Fluctuations options	1	1	1	1	

the contract administrator should not be concerned about recommending MW05 for the type of straightforward project for which it was intended.

Some general principles of contract law

Formation

1.21 A contract is formed when an unconditional offer is unconditionally accepted. In the context of a building project, where contractors have been invited to submit competitive tenders, the tenders constitute an 'offer' to carry out the work shown in the tender documents for the price tendered. If a tender is accepted then a contract will have been formed, and the terms of the contract will be those set out or referred to in the tender documents.

1.22   'Letters of intent' can cloud the picture and should be avoided. If it is possible to accept the tender without qualification then it is better simply to write a letter to that effect, and the contract comes into existence from the moment the letter has been received by the contractor. (For a more detailed analysis of the formation of contract the reader could refer to Aeberli *Focus on Construction Contract Formation.*) The effect of a letter expressing an intention to enter into a contract at some point in the future will depend on the wording and circumstances in each case, but it is likely to be of no legal effect. Starting work on such a basis could have disastrous consequences for both parties.

1.23   If there is a period of negotiation, careful records should be kept of all matters agreed in order that they can be accurately incorporated into the formal Contract Documents. These documents should always be prepared as soon as agreement is reached, and before start on site. Failure to execute the documents does not necessarily mean that no contract is in existence, but can often lead to avoidable arguments about what was agreed.

Express terms

1.24   Generally speaking, parties are bound by the terms of the contract which they have expressly set out and agreed. In practice there may be difficulties in establishing exactly what these terms are: they may be scattered amongst several documents, they may be ambiguous or contradictory, or they may be silent on some aspect of the matter under dispute. The process of piecing together and interpreting the terms of a contract is governed by a distinct area of law. Some of the more important rules are:

- Words should be given their ordinary literal meaning; where there is ambiguity or a conflict, generally a court will determine, on an objective basis, what it considers were the true intentions of the parties. For example, specially agreed terms will normally prevail over standard printed terms, as these are more likely to represent the parties' intentions. However, this would not apply to MW05 as it contains a clause which states that the printed terms prevail.

- The contract is usually construed most strongly against the party who drew it up (termed the *contra proferentem* rule). It is generally considered, however, that this rule would not apply to JCT standard forms that are negotiated, rather than drawn up by one party. It may nevertheless apply to other Contract Documents such as the specification, unless the terms in question had been specifically negotiated, and may also apply to the form itself if it has been amended in significant respects.

- Generally speaking, evidence of previous negotiations is not admissible to contradict the express terms of the contract (*Wates Construction* v *Bredero Fleet*), though evidence of the factual background may be used in relation to implied terms (see para 1.25 below).

Wates Construction (South) Ltd v Bredero Fleet Ltd (1993) 63 BLR 128

Wates Construction were employed on JCT80 to build a shopping centre for Bredero. Some sub-structural work differed from that shown on the drawings and disputes arose regarding the valuation of the Works, which were taken to arbitration. In establishing conditions under which, under the contract, it had been assumed the work would be carried out, the arbitrator took into account pre-tender negotiations and the actual knowledge that Wates gained as a result of the negotiations, including proposals that had been put forward at that time. Wates appealed and the court found that the arbitrator had erred by taking this extrinsic information into consideration. The conditions under which the Works had to be executed had to be derived from the express provisions of the bills, drawings and other Contract Documents.

Implied terms

1.25   In addition to the interpretative rules outlined above, there are several mechanisms whereby terms which the parties have not expressly set out may be implied into a contract.

1.26   A term can be implied 'in fact' or 'in law'. Terms are implied in fact to give effect to the presumed but unexpressed intentions of the parties and will not be implied if they would contradict the express terms. They are implied on the basis of the particular circumstances of that contract and normally must survive a 'test of necessity'; in other words, that without the implication the contract would be so un-businesslike that no sensible person would ever have agreed to it. The courts have not always applied the test with this degree of stringency, and will sometimes imply a term on the basis that it appears the parties intended it.

1.27   In addition, the courts' approach to the range of circumstances that can be looked at, sometimes referred to as the 'factual matrix', has varied considerably from a broad approach taking into account a wide variety of surrounding circumstances, to a very narrow one which confines itself to the 'four corners' of the Contract Documents. (A typical 'narrow' approach is shown in *Wates Construction (South) Ltd* v *Bredero Fleet* in para 1.24 above, but the exception in *Rotherham MBC* v *Frank Haslam Milan* (1996) discussed in para 1.33 below should also be noted.) In practice it would be unwise to rely on a term being implied on the basis of the surrounding circumstances.

1.28   Terms are implied in law where either (a) they are always implied into that type of contract as a matter of legal incidence or (b) through the operation of statute. In either case the term is not based on the presumed intention of the parties. The fact that a term contradicts the express terms of a contract will not necessarily prevent its being implied. An example of terms implied as a necessary incidence is certain obligations that would always be implied into contracts between landlord and tenant. By far the most important implied terms with respect to construction contracts are those implied by statutes. The most significant of these statutes are the Sale of Goods Act 1979, the Supply of Goods and Services Act 1982 (both amended by the Sale and Supply of Goods Act 1994), the Defective Premises Act 1972 and the Housing Grants, Construction and Regeneration Act 1996.

The Sale of Goods Act 1979

1.29   This implies terms into contracts for the sale of goods regarding title (s.123 Correspondence with description, s.131 Quality and fitness for purpose, s.14 Implied terms about quality or fitness, and s.15 Sale by sample). For example section 14 implies a term that where the seller sells goods in the course of business and the buyer, expressly or by implication, makes known to the seller any particular purpose for which the goods are being bought, there is an implied condition that the goods supplied under the contract will be reasonably fit for that purpose.

The Supply of Goods and Services Act 1982

1.30   This covers contracts for work and materials, contracts for the hire of goods, and contracts for services. Most construction contracts come under the category of 'work and materials' and the Act implies terms into these equivalent to sections 12–15 listed above with respect to any goods in which the property has been transferred under the contract. So, as above, any materials supplied should be reasonably fit for their intended purpose, provided always that the buyer is relying on the supplier's skill and judgement. (If the buyer specifies a particular material then this would be sufficient to show that it was not relying on the seller.) For services, the Act implies terms regarding care and skill, time of performance and consideration. For example section 14 implies a term that where the supplier is acting in the course of business, the supplier will carry out the services within a reasonable time, provided of course the parties have not themselves agreed terms regarding time.

The Defective Premises Act 1972

1.31   This applies where work is carried out in connection with a dwelling, including design work. It states that 'a person taking on work in connection with the provision of a dwelling owes a duty to see that the work which he takes on is done in a workmanlike or, as the case may be, professional manner, with proper materials and so that as regards that work the dwelling will be fit for habitation when completed' (s.1(1)). This appears to be a strict liability, and is owed to anyone acquiring an interest in the dwelling.

The Housing Grants, Construction and Regeneration Act 1996

1.32   This requires that all construction contracts falling within the definition of the Act contain certain provisions including the right to stage payments, the right to notice of the amount to be paid, the right to suspend work for non-payment, and the right to take any dispute arising out of the contract to adjudication. If the parties fail to include these provisions in their contract, the Act will imply terms to provide these rights (s.114) by means of the Scheme for Construction Contracts (England and Wales) Regulations 1998. The Act is of broad application but with one important exception in the context of minor works – it does not apply to a 'construction contract' (defined in section 104 of the Act) with a residential occupier. This means a contract relating to operations on a dwelling that one of the parties to the contract occupies or intends to occupy (s.106). However, work on other residential properties, for example for landlords, local authorities or housing associations, will usually be covered by the Act. Also, it should be noted that a sub-contract dispute might still be covered even where the main contract involves a residential occupier.

Liability for design

1.33   The law distinguishes between two levels of liability, which are reflected in the above legislation. When a professional undertakes design he or she is normally under an express or implied duty to exercise that degree of skill and care expected of an ordinary competent professional. When a contractor undertakes design, courts would normally assume that the completed design should be 'fit for purpose' unless the parties have indicated anything to the contrary in their contract. The above statutes do not cover the situation where a contractor designs and constructs a building; this assumption is derived precedence set by well established case law (*e.g. Viking Grain v T. H. White*). These two levels of liability differ significantly, the second being more onerous than the first. Under the second, which is often referred to as a 'strict' level of liability, any party bringing a claim simply has to show that the product/component/building designed by the contractor is not fit for purpose, whereas in the first it also has to show that the designer did not use the required level of skill and care.

Viking Grain Storage Ltd v T. H. White and another (1985) 33 BLR 103

Viking Grain entered into a contract with White to design and erect a grain drying and storage installation to handle 10,000 tons of grain. After it was complete Viking commenced proceedings against the contractor claiming that, because of defects, the grain store was unfit for its intended use. The contractor in its defence claimed that there was no implied warranty in the contract that the finished product would be fit for purpose, and that the contractor's obligation was limited to the use of reasonable skill and care in carrying out the design. The judge decided that Viking had been relying on the contractor and that there was an implied warranty that not only the materials supplied but also the whole installation should be fit for the required purpose. There could be no differentiation between reliance placed with regard to the quality of the materials and to the design.

The court also made it clear that the contractor's liability was strict, in other words that the contractor was liable irrespective of whether it had exercised a reasonable level of skill and care in carrying out the design. This is a more onerous level of liability than that assumed by someone undertaking design services only, where they would normally be required to demonstrate that they had exercised the skill and care of a competent member of their profession. The fact that the building was defective was sufficient to prove that there had been a breach of contract, without the employer having to prove that the contractor had been negligent.

Rotherham MBC v Frank Haslam Milan and M. J. Gleeson (1996) 78 BLR 1

A contract (JCT63) to construct a new office building involved the laying of fill on the site and the contractor, Gleeson, was given a detailed specification as to the material of the fill: '... hardcore shall be graded or uncrushed gravel, rock fill, crushed concrete or slag or natural sand or a combination of any of these.' The clause omitted to state the types of slag that could be used and the unweathered steel slag selected by the contractor proved to be expansive, causing cracking in the concrete ground floor slab (around £700,000 worth of damage).

The Court of Appeal, overturning the decision of the Official Referee at first instance, found the contractor was not liable for the damage caused by the heave. The court stated, among other things, that the fact that the employer had engaged a contract administrator to write the specification showed the employer did not intend to rely on the skill and expertise of the contractor in selecting the hardcore. If it had not been for these special circumstances, however, the court stated that it would have found the contractor strictly liable for providing a slag that was fit for the purpose for which it was to be used. It should be noted that Rotherham was concerned with an omission within the design information, and that the Court of Appeal made it clear that it was not the express terms of JCT63 that prevented the contractor assuming design liability, but the surrounding circumstances. If the parties had made it clear, for example through the specification or a note on a drawing, that they were relying on the contractor to select a suitable slag, then the outcome might have been different.

Exemption clauses

1.34   The scope for excluding liability for important matters is limited by two significant pieces of legislation, the Unfair Contract Terms Act 1977, and the Unfair Terms in Consumer Contracts Regulations 1994.

Unfair Contract Terms Act 1977

1.35   This has the effect of rendering various exclusion clauses void including any clauses excluding liability for death or personal injury resulting from negligence, any clauses attempting to exclude liability for Sale of Goods Act 1979 section 12 obligations (and the equivalent under the Supply of Goods and Services Act), any clauses attempting to exclude liability for Sale of Goods Act 1979 section 13, 14 or 15 obligations (and the equivalent under the Supply of Goods and Services Act) where they are operating against any person dealing as consumer. It also renders certain other exclusion clauses void in so far as they fail to satisfy a test of reasonableness, for example liability for negligence other than liability for death or personal injury, and liability for breach of section 13, 14 and 15 obligations in contracts which do not involve a consumer.

Unfair Terms in Consumer Contracts Regulations 1999

1.36   These only apply to terms in contracts between a seller of goods or supplier of goods and services and a consumer, and where the terms have not been individually negotiated (this would generally include all standard forms). A consumer is defined as a person who, in making a contract, is acting 'for purposes which are outside his trade, business or profession' (s.3(1)). An 'unfair term' is any term that causes a significant imbalance in the parties' rights to the detriment of the consumer, and the regulations state that any such term will not be binding on the consumer. An indicative list of terms is given in Schedule 2 and includes, for example, 'any term excluding or hindering the consumer's right to take legal action or exercise any other legal remedy, particularly by requiring the consumer to take disputes exclusively to arbitration.' It is important, therefore, that if the arbitration option is selected, or if any other amendments are made which could be seen as limiting the employer's rights, these have been explained and discussed, in order that they can be considered to have been individually negotiated.

1.37   JCT forms are amended from time to time in response to new legislation and other changes in the law. The matters outlined above have been taken into account within

MW05, and some will be referred to later in this book. It is nevertheless important to understand the legislative background to the form. Not only can the law operate to imply terms where the parties have omitted to set out their requirements, for example over the quality of goods and materials, but legislation may operate to override amendments the parties have made to the form, or to render specifically agreed terms void. An example of the former would be if the parties attempted to delete terms of the contract which are required by the Housing Grants, Construction and Regeneration Act 1996. Unless the Act did not apply to that contract, the deletion would be ineffective, as those terms will then be implied through operation of the Scheme. An example of the latter would be if the contractor qualified its tender by inserting clauses excluding liability for injury caused by defective materials. These terms would be void even if they were included in the executed Contract Documents.

2 Documents

2.1 Documents are central to the success of all building operations, even to small projects such as those carried out under MW05. In fact with many small jobs on a short programme and tight budget, full and accurate information is essential right from the outset.

Contract Documents

2.2 MW05 defines 'Contract Documents' under the second recital (or the third in MWD05). This indicates that any or all of the following documents can be prepared on behalf of the employer:

- drawings;

- specification;

- work schedules;

- Employer's Requirements (MWD05 only);

- conditions;

- schedule of rates.

2.3 The parties are required to delete the items that will not be used, and the remaining items, together with the printed Conditions, comprise the 'Contract Documents'. Interestingly, as 'drawings' are indicated as an item that may be deleted, it would in theory be possible to let the contract on a works schedule, or on Employer's Requirements alone, but in practice drawings will almost always form part of the Contract Documents. Also, as the contract is not intended to be used as a 'design-build' contract, the Employer's Requirements will normally cover only part of the Works, with the rest described by drawings plus schedules and/or a specification.

2.4 There is no provision for a bill of quantities. The contractor will normally price either the specification or the schedules in an itemised format, or provide a Contract Sum backed by a schedule of rates (third recital, or fourth recital in MWD05). Although in theory this article could be deleted, and the contractor tender a lump sum figure on the basis of drawings alone, this will be impracticable as the priced document will be used, if relevant, in the valuing of variations. To be useful, therefore, the price breakdown will have to be reasonably comprehensive and detailed.

2.5 The 'Contract Drawings' are listed under the second recital (the third recital in MWD05). These should all be identified precisely, including revision numbers, etc. The list may be annexed if long, but if so the list must be clearly identified. Note that in MW05 there is no reference to who prepared the drawings.

2.6   A specification should normally form part of the documentation, as it is inadvisable to rely on notes on drawings except on the smallest of jobs. The CPI recommendation is that the specification becomes the core document in terms of defining quality, and that the drawings and other documents cross-refer to clauses in the specification.

2.7   MW05 does not describe what is meant by the term 'schedule', nor indicate what form the schedule should take. In practice it is generally a 'schedule of work', and could be arranged by work sections, by trades, or on a room-by-room basis as is common in refurbishment work. In all cases it is likely to be clearer if the detailed specification information is kept in a separate part of the document, or bound separately, and referred to by the schedules. Where two documents are used, it might be more satisfactory for the contractor to price the itemised schedule.

2.8   The Contractor should be sent copies of all the intended Contract Documents at time of tender, together with all the information required under the Contract Particulars, namely commencement and completion dates (cl 2·2, or 2·3 in MWD05), liquidated damages (cl 2·8, or 2·9), the rectification period (cl 2·10, or 2·11), the retention percentage (cl 4·3 and 4·5), the period for supply of documentation (cl 4·8·1), together with information relating to tax, fluctuations, insurance and dispute resolution. For good practice in preparation and co-ordination of the specification, drawings and schedules, see current relevant publications on Co-ordinated Project Information (CPI). The contract requires that the parties sign the Contract Documents.

Health and safety documents

2.9   Clauses 3·9·1 to 3·9·4 will be applicable where the Contract Particulars indicate that the project is notifiable under the Construction (Design and Management) Regulations (CDM) 2007 (entry relating to the fifth or sixth recitals). These clauses refer to the various obligations that arise out of statute, and in addition make some of them contractual obligations. Particularly important in this respect are matters relating to the Construction Phase Plan, and the Health and Safety File.

2.10   The Construction Phase Plan is not a Contract Document under MW05, and the recitals make no mention of it having been prepared and given to the contractor at the time of tender. Nevertheless, it is a statutory obligation for the employer to ensure that a Construction Phase Plan is prepared before construction work begins (Regulation 16). The employer must provide the contractor with pre-construction information, which is sent out with the tender documents. Before any construction work can begin the contractor must have developed the Plan to comply with regulation 23 and supplied a copy to the employer (cl 3·9·2). To avoid uncertainty, it is advisable to require that this document be submitted by the contractor well in advance of start of work on site. It should be noted that following Amendment 1 the contract now requires that a pre-construction 'CDM Planning Period' is identified on the Contract Particulars, to allow time for planning and preparation in accordance with Regulation 10(2)(c).

2.11   The Health and Safety File is principally a matter for the CDM co-ordinator who will compile it, but there is a requirement on the contractor to provide information for this File, and to ensure any sub-contractor also complies. Under clause 2·9 (2·10 in MWD05) the contract administrator, before certifying practical completion, must make sure that the contractor has 'sufficiently complied' with this requirement.

Execution

2.12   The articles of agreement and the Contract Particulars must be completed with care, and the appropriate deletions made. The articles form the heart of the agreement whereby the contractor undertakes to carry out and complete the Works 'in accordance with the Contract Documents' (Article 1), and in return the employer undertakes to pay the contractor the Contract Sum as adjusted in accordance with the Conditions (Article 2). The articles of agreement contain the attestation that must be signed by both parties. The contract may be executed under hand or as a deed (see the Notes on Execution in the form), and in the latter case the form provides for execution by the parties as individuals or as companies. (Note that the edition for use in Scotland contains special provisions for signing in accordance with the Requirements in Writing (Scotland) Act 1995.) In addition the appropriate entries must be made in the Contract Particulars. Detailed guidance on completing the form can be found in *MW05 Contract Administration Guide*, and in the footnotes under the Contract Particulars.

Use of documents

Interpretation, definitions

2.13   MW05 sets out a list of definitions in clause 1·1, some of which cross-refer to the recitals or to definitions embodied in the text clauses, for example 'insolvent'. The payment provisions in MW05 refer to the issue of notices and periods of time all as required by the HGCRA 1996. Clauses 1·4 and 1·6 also restate the requirements of the Act concerning the serving of notices and the calculation of periods of days. Clause 1·5 excludes the rights of third parties to bring actions to enforce the terms of the contract (which they might otherwise have under the Contracts (Rights of Third Parties) Act 1999). Clause 1·7 states that the law of contract will be English law.

Priority of Contract Documents

2.14   Clause 1·2 states that the agreement and conditions are to be read as a whole, but that nothing contained in the Contract Drawings, the contract specification or the work schedules (or, in MWD05, the Employer's Requirements) 'shall override or modify this Agreement or these Conditions'. If this clause were not included, the position under common law would be the reverse; in other words, anything specifically agreed and stated in a document would normally override any standard provisions.

2.15   If the parties wish to agree special terms that differ in any way from the printed Conditions, then amendments must be made to the actual form. If necessary, due to lack of space, these amendments could refer to the special terms, which could be appended to the form or included in the specification. However, amending standard forms is unwise without expert advice, as the consequential effects are difficult to predict. Deleting the latter part of clause 1·2 could be particularly unwise as it may have unintended effects on other parts of the contract.

2.16   In theory, additional provisions that supplement but do not override the printed Conditions would be binding. It might be wise, though, especially where the supplementary condition is particularly significant, to make specific reference to it in the printed form.

Inconsistencies, errors or omissions

2.17   Apart from the priority given to the printed Conditions, there is no statement about which of the other documents used will take priority, should a conflict arise. Clause 2·4 (2·5 in MWD05) requires inconsistencies in or between the Contract Documents, including in the case of MWD05 the Employer's Requirements, to be corrected, and any such is treated as a variation. The normal practice is for the contract administrator to issue an instruction regarding the correction, although the contract does not specifically require this. The contractor is required to correct any inconsistencies in the documents it prepares for the CDP works 'after the Architect/Contract Administrator has expressed his reasonable satisfaction as to the manner in which the Contractor proposes to deal with the discrepancy' (cl 2·5·2). A reasonable objection would be that the correction would result in the work not complying with the Employer's Requirements. Because of clause 2·1·6, the proposal should be put forward at least seven days prior to the intended date of starting the relevant work (see 5.11).

2.18   If the contractor finds any divergence between the Contract Documents (including in the case of MWD05 the Employer's Requirements) or any instruction of the contract administrator, and Statutory Requirements, then the contract administrator must be given immediate written notice (cl 2·5·1, or 2·6·2 in MWD05). Once a divergence is discovered, the contract administrator should issue an instruction to clarify the situation and, as above, this instruction would be treated as a variation, provided the contractor has complied with its duty to notify, the contractor would not be liable if the works did not comply with Statutory Requirements.

2.19   Except in the case of divergences from Statutory Requirements, the contractor is not under any express obligation to point out any inconsistencies that it finds within or between the Contract Documents. The contract also does not place any obligation on the contractor to search for discrepancies etc. However, the general duty to use reasonable skill and care would suggest some degree of observance could be expected. If the contractor fails to point out discrepancies that it notices, or should have noticed, and work has to be re-built as a result, then it is suggested that the contractor may lose the right to extra payment, or an extension of time. This is only likely to be the case where the matter is so obvious that no competent contractor could have missed it, and is unlikely to apply to errors within the Employer's Requirements, including divergences from Statutory Requirements, as MWD05 makes it clear the contractor is not responsible for their contents (cl 2·1·2).

Custody and control of documents

2.20 MW05 contains no provisions as to custody and control of documents. The original signed Contract Documents would normally remain in the custody of the contract administrator, who should store them safely and retain working copies for reference throughout the life of the contract and beyond. It is normal practice to provide the employer and the contractor with certified copies.

2.21 The documents provided should not be used for any purpose other than the Works, and the details of the rates or prices should not be divulged. The contractor should be required to keep one copy of all of the Contract Documents and information issued by the contract administrator on site at all reasonable times. All drawings, etc, which bear the name of the contract administrator should be returned upon final payment.

Sub-contract documents

2.22 JCT Ltd publishes a generic short form of sub-contract (ShortSub) that may be used with MW05, although MW05 does not require that it is used, and in practice on small projects it is unlikely that the employer will insist on the use of a particular form. MW05 does, however, include some restrictions on the terms that may be agreed for any sub-contract. These are set out in clauses 3·3·2 and 3·3·3 and relate to the right to interest on unpaid amounts properly due to the sub-contractor from the contractor, and that the contract between contractor and sub-contractor shall terminate immediately upon the termination of the contractor's employment under this contract. There are no requirements that particular conditions relating to ownership of unfixed goods and materials are included, such as those that are required by SBC05 or IC05, which could in some circumstances leave the employer at risk. The JCT intend to publish a Minor Works Sub-Contract with sub-contractor's design (MWSub/d), for use with MWD05, but at the time of writing this is not yet available. Any sub-contract should also, of course, comply with the relevant requirements of the HGCRA 1996, otherwise the terms of the Scheme for Construction Contracts would be implied.

3 Obligations of the contractor

3.1   The contractor's paramount obligation is to 'carry out and complete the Works'. This is stated in article 1, and reinforced in clause 2·1. A court would normally hold the contractor wholly responsible for achieving this, irrespective of whether the contract administrator visits the site. Clause 3·0·1 also makes it clear that this obligation is not reduced in any way if some of the work is sub-contracted.

The Works

3.2   The Works that the contractor undertakes to carry out will be as briefly described in the first recital of MW05, and as shown or described in the Contract Documents. It is therefore important to check that the entry in the first recital clearly identifies the nature and scope of the proposed work, and that descriptions of the Works given elsewhere are clear and adequate.

3.3   Note that the Works will also include any changes subsequently brought about by a contract administrator's instruction, which might also introduce additional drawings or other information. These might not be 'Contract Documents', but they nevertheless have an important status and the contractor is obliged to carry out any additional work that they show.

Design

3.4   MWD05 makes provision for the contractor to undertake the design of part or parts of the project. This is brought about by the second recital (MWD05 only), which allows the parties to agree that the 'Works' will include the design and construction of identified parts, termed the 'Contractor's Designed Portion' (the 'CDP'). It will be important to identify the parts precisely. If this provision is to be used, the arrangement must be clearly explained to the employer, preferably at appointment stage, and confirmed in writing, as the architect has no authority to delegate design responsibilities without the agreement of the employer (*Moresk Cleaners* v *Hicks*).

Moresk Cleaners Ltd v Thomas Henwood Hicks (1966) 4 BLR 50

Moresk Cleaners employed Thomas Hicks, an architect, to prepare plans and specifications for an extension to their laundry. Although the building was built according to the plans and specifications, the design of the structure had in fact been delegated by the architect to the contractor. Within two years cracks appeared in the structure and the roof purlins sagged. Moresk Cleaners brought a claim against the architect, who argued that it was an implied term of his contract that he should be able to delegate the design to the contractor, or alternatively that he had authority to employ the contractor on behalf of Moresk. The court found that there was no such implied term and that the architect had no such authority.

3.5   The contractor's design obligation is set out under clause 2·1·1, which states 'The Contractor shall, using reasonable skill, care and diligence, complete the design for the Contractor's Designed Portion including, so far as not described or stated in the Employer's Requirements, the selection of any specifications for the kinds and standards of the materials, goods and workmanship to be used in the CDP Works'.

3.6   This level of design liability is less than that which would normally be implied by law (see paragraph 1.31), i.e. a strict obligation to supply something fit for purpose, but is instead an obligation to use reasonable skill and care. In effect, this means that in order to prove a breach the employer would need to prove that the contractor had been negligent. If, for example, the contractor is required to design a heating system to heat the rooms to a certain temperature, and when installed it fails to do so, this fact alone would not be enough to prove that there had been a breach of contract. The employer would need to prove that the contractor had failed to use the required level of skill and care.

3.7   It is also slightly different wording to the equivalent clauses in other JCT forms, which require the contractor to use the skill and care of 'an appropriately qualified and competent professional designer'. MWD05 instead requires a 'reasonable level of skill and care'. Whereas in many contexts these may be the same level, in some a 'reasonable' level might be less. For example, on a project using a small firm of builders, it might not be reasonable to expect the same level of design skill as would be provided by a competent professional designer.

3.8   In drafting these clauses the JCT have taken a practical approach, which reflects the reality of smaller projects where more stringent requirements may result in unacceptably high tenders. However it is important that the contract administrator and employer understand the implications of the clause, and if a higher level of liability is required, the employer may need to consider using another form, or take legal advice.

3.9   MWD05 clause 2·1·2 makes it clear that the contractor is not responsible for the adequacy of the information in the Employer's Requirements. Where the Employer's Requirements contain an outline design, which the contractor is required to complete, the contractor is not responsible for checking the adequacy of the design that has been provided. If any inadequacy is found in any design contained in the Requirements, then the contract administrator would need to issue an instruction to remedy this. The contractor is required to comply with directions of the contract administrator with regard to the design of the CDP with the Works as a whole (cl 2·1·3) and, although the contract does not specifically cover the point, it is generally assumed that the contract administrator is responsible for the overall coordination of the design.

Materials, goods and workmanship: MW05

3.10   Under MW05 work must be carried out in a workmanlike manner and in accordance with the Health and Safety Plan (cl 2·1·1). Under clause 2·1·1 (MW05 only) the contractor is obliged to carry out the Works in compliance with the Contract Documents, which would include providing materials, workmanship etc to the standards specified. This obligation is not qualified by use of the phrase 'so far as procurable', as is the case in some other standard forms. If a specified material was unavailable at the time required, it is suggested that the contractor would remain under an obligation to provide a close substitute, subject to the contract administrator's approval. If this constitutes a variation the contractor may then, however, be entitled to an extension of time and to an adjustment to the Contract Sum as a consequence. Failure to do so can be grounds for determination by the employer under clause 6·4·1·2.

3.11   Clause 2·1·2 states:

> Where and to the extent that approval of the quality of materials or of the standards of workmanship is a matter for the opinion of the Architect/Contract Administrator such quality and standards shall be to his reasonable satisfaction.

This phrase does not authorise the architect to alter the standard specified at will, but means that where a correct construction of the Contract Documents leaves a matter regarding quality to the discretion of the contract administrator, the contractor only fulfils its obligations if the contract administrator is satisfied. It is suggested that any expression of dissatisfaction by the contract administrator must be made within a reasonable period of the carrying out of the work. The contract administrator should generally avoid using phrases such as 'to approval' or 'to the contract administrator's satisfaction' in the Contract Documents, as it leaves much scope for argument about what standard might be reasonable. It should be noted, however, that in MW05 no certificate subsequently issued by the contract administrator is stated to be conclusive as to the contract administrator's satisfaction with such work (see 7·26–7·28).

3.12   If the phrase 'or otherwise approved' is used in a specification or bill of quantities this does not mean that the contract administrator must be prepared to consider alternatives put forward by the contractor, nor that the contract administrator must give any reasons for rejecting alternatives (*Leedsford* v *City of Bradford*). It merely gives the contract administrator the right to do so. A substitution would always constitute a variation whether or not this phrase is present in the specification.

Leedsford Ltd v The Lord Mayor, Alderman and Citizens of the City of Bradford (1956) 24 BLR 45 (CA)

In a contract for the provision of a new infant school the contract bills stated 'Artificial Stone... The following to be obtained from the Empire Stone Company Limited, 326 Deansgate, or other approved firm...'. During the course of the contract the contractor obtained quotes from other companies and sent them to the architect for approval. The architect, however, insisted that Empire Stone was used and as Empire Stone was considerably more expensive the contractor brought a claim for damages for breach of contract. The court dismissed the claim, stating 'The builder agrees to supply artificial stone. The stone has to be Empire Stone unless the parties agree some other stone, and no other stone can be substituted except by mutual agreement. The builder fulfils his contract if he provides Empire Stone, whether the Bradford Corporation want it or not; and the Corporation Architect can say that he will approve of no other stone except the Empire Stone' (Hodson J at page 58).

Materials, goods and workmanship: MWD05

3.13   Under MWD05 the clauses that deal with standard of work and materials are somewhat different to those under MW05. The contractor is required to carry out the Works in accordance with the Contract Documents (cl 2·1), so for work which is not part of the Contractor's Designed Portion, the contractor would be obliged to comply with any specification provided. The form also contains an equivalent provision regarding work which is to be to the approval of the contract administrator (clause 2·2·1).

3.14   With respect to the Contractor's Designed Portion, the contractor must provide materials, goods etc as specified in the Employer's Requirements or, if none are specified, use reasonable skill and care in selecting such material and goods. Work required to be 'to approval' is similarly covered by clause 2·2·1. Clause 2·2·1 of MWD05 then continues:

> To the extent that the quality of materials and goods or standards of workmanship are neither described ... nor stated to be a matter for such opinion or satisfaction, they shall in the case of the Contractor's Designed Portion be of a standard appropriate to it and shall in any other case be of a standard appropriate to the Works.

This reflects the duty that would normally be implied by law, in other words where the description of the standard required for any goods, materials and workmanship is (deliberately or inadvertently) incomplete, the contractor is required to provide something 'fit for purpose'. This appears to be a strict obligation (see above), rather than an obligation to use reasonable skill and care. There is therefore something of a tension between clauses 2·1·1 and 2·2·1 of MWD05. It is suggested that the correct interpretation is that the contractor is under a strict liability to provide materials, goods etc of an appropriate quality for non-CDP items, and under the lesser obligation to use due skill and care regarding all other design forming part of the CDP, but the exact interpretation of these clauses may need to be determined by the courts. What is interesting to note is that the clause quoted above does not appear in MW05, therefore this form does not cover the situation where the specification of a material etc is omitted. For MW05 it will be open to argument what level of responsibility, if any, the contractor has with respect to such missing items (see paragraph 1.31).

3.15   In summary, the contractor's responsibility for work and materials in the two forms is as follows:

- if specified or described in the Contract Documents, to provide materials etc as specified;

- if the contract requires them to be approved by the contract administrator, to be to his or her reasonable satisfaction;

- if not specified at all, with respect to the CDP, to be a standard appropriate to the CDP (with some ambiguity over the level of liability);

- if not specified at all, with respect to non-CPD items, in the case of MWD05, to be a standard appropriate to the Works (with some ambiguity over the level of liability);

- if not specified at all, in the case of MW05, the obligations of the contractor will depend on the particular provisions agreed, and whether a term may be implied regarding design liability.

Obligations in respect of quality of sub-contracted work

3.16   It is common practice today, even on small jobs, for much building work to be sub-contracted. This arrangement benefits the employer, who has the advantage of a wider range of skills than is normally found in the traditional building company, without any of the problems of direct responsibility for appointment of sub-contractors.

3.17   MW05 provides for domestic sub-contractors only, and there are no provisions for naming or nominating firms selected by the employer or contract administrator. The contract makes it clear that the contractor remains fully responsible for the standards and quality of all sub-contracted work, which would include any part of any Contractor's Designed Portion which had been sub-contracted (cl 3·3·1).

Compliance with statute

3.18   The contractor is under a statutory duty to comply with all legislation that is relevant to the carrying out of the work, for example in respect of goods and services, building and construction regulations, and health and safety. The duty is absolute and there is no possibility of contracting out of any of the resulting obligations.

3.19   Both MW05 and MWD05 introduce a contractual duty in addition to the statutory duty, which provides protection to the employer. Clause 2·1 requires the contractor to comply with, and give all notices required by the 'Statutory Requirements' which are defined as including any statute, statutory instrument, regulation, rule or order or any bylaw applicable to the Works. As discussed in Section 2, if the contractor finds any divergence between the Contract Documents, including in the case of MWD05 the Employer's Requirements, or any instruction of the contract administrator, and Statutory Requirements, then it must notify the contract administrator immediately (cl 2·5·1, or 2·6·2 in MWD05), who should then issue an instruction to clarify the situation. Provided it complies with its obligation to notify the contractor administrator, the contractor is not liable for work which does not comply with statute, if the non-compliance resulted from carrying out work in accordance with the Contract Documents or further instructions issued by the contract administrator (cl 2·5·2, or 2·6·2 in MWD05). The contractor is required to pay all fees and charges 'legally demandable' (cl 2·6, or 2·7 in MWD05), and such payments are stated not to be reimbursable, unless otherwise agreed.

Health and safety legislation

3.20   The appropriate deletion in the Contract Particulars (fifth or sixth recital) should indicate whether or not the project is notifiable under the CDM Regulations. Where it is, the contractor would be obliged to give statutory notice to the Health and Safety Executive before carrying out any construction work.

Figure 5 Key obligations of the contractor

Clause (MW/MWD)	Obligation of the contractor
2·1·1/2·1	Carry out and complete the Works
/2·1·1	Complete the design of the CDP
/2·1·3	Comply with contract administrator's directions regarding integration of the CDP
/2·1·5	Provide drawings and information to explain the CDP
2·1·3/2·2·2	Take all reasonable steps to encourage employees, etc to be registered under the Construction Skills Certification Scheme
2·2/2·3	Complete the Works by the date for completion
/2·5·2	Correct inconsistencies between CDP documents
2·5·1/2·6·1	Notify the contract administrator of any divergence found between Statutory Requirements and the Contract Documents and any instruction of the contract administrator
2·6/2·7	Pay statutory fees and charges
2·7/2·8	Notify the contract administrator when it appears the Works will not be completed by the date for completion for reasons beyond the contractor's control
2·8·1/2·9·1	Pay the employer liquidated damages for failure to complete by the date for completion
2·10/2·11	Make good defects which appear within three months of practical completion
3·2	Keep a person in charge on the site at all reasonable times
3·3	Ensure that any sub-contract includes specified conditions
3·4	To forthwith carry out all instructions issued by the contract administrator
3·6·2	Endeavour to agree the value of variations with the contract administrator
3·9	Comply with the CDM Regulations
4·8·1	Provide the contract administrator with all documentation reasonably required for finalising the final account
4·9	Pay simple interest to the employer on any amount not properly paid in regard to the final certificate
5·1	Indemnify the employer for any expense, liability, loss, claim or proceedings in respect of injury to or death of any person
5·2	Indemnify the employer for any damage to property
5·3	Take out effective insurance against its liability
5·4A	Take out insurance against loss or damage to the Works as required
5·5	Produce evidence of insurance
6·11·2	Prepare an account following termination under clauses 6·8 to 6·10

3.21   Where all the CDM Regulations apply the employer must appoint a CDM co-ordinator who will be the contract administrator or some other person who is to be named in article 4. If that person ceases to be the CDM co-ordinator the employer must appoint another person and notify the contractor accordingly (cl 3·10). Clause 3·9·1 places a contractual obligation on the employer to ensure that the CDM co-ordinator carries out his or her duties under the Regulations. This is a wider obligation than the 'reasonable satisfaction with competence' obligation imposed by the Regulations. Breach of it gives the contractor the right to determine the contract under clause 6·8·1·3. What is more likely to happen is that the contractor will claim for an extension of time. An example might be where a CDM co-ordinator delays in commenting on a contractor's proposed amendment to the Construction Phase Plan, and progress is thereby delayed.

3.22   Clause 3·9 places a duty on the contractor, if acting as the principal contractor referred to in article 5, to comply with all the relevant duties set out in the Regulations. It is an express requirement that the contractor must develop the Construction Phase Plan to comply with the Regulations before 'carrying out any construction work'.

3.23   Breach of this duty is grounds for determination under clause 6·4·1·3. A specified default notice (cl 6·4·2) still has to be given, and JCT Practice Note 27 suggests that this provision should only be used in situations where the Health and Safety Executive is likely to close the site.

3.24   The contractor is obliged to send any modification of the Construction Phase Plan to the employer, the CDM co-ordinator and the contract administrator (cl 3·9·2·1). This may occur, for example, due to unexpected site conditions.

3.25   The contractor should take the cost of developing the Construction Phase Plan into account at tender stage, and no claims should be entertained for adjusting it to suit the contractor's or sub-contractor's working methods. If alterations are needed as a result of an instruction requiring a variation, then the costs would be included in the valuation of the variation, and the alterations should be taken into account in assessing any application for extension of time.

Other obligations

3.26   In addition to the major obligations outlined above, the contractor also has other obligations arising out of the contract. Most significant of these are in relation to progress and programming, discussed in Chapter 4, and in regard to insurance matters, discussed in Chapter 8. The contractor's obligations are summarised in Figure 5.

4 Commencement and completion

4.1 There are two paramount dates in any building contract: (1) the date for possession or commencement and (2) the date for completion of the work. It is preferable that actual dates are given at the time of tendering. Vague indications such as 'to be agreed' or 'eight weeks after approval by' should be avoided, as the start date and duration can considerably affect the tender figure, particularly in the case of smaller jobs on a tight programme. In the event that work is started without proper agreement over dates, the contract will be subject to the Supply of Goods and Services Act 1982, which states that completion is to be within a reasonable time.

4.2 The MW05 'Contract Particulars' require a date for commencement of the Works, and a date for completion (cl 2·2, or 2·3 in MWD05). However, as printed, MW05 does not allow for either commencement or completion in stages. If work needs to be carried out in contractually binding phases, then it would be necessary to set this out in detail in the Contract Documents, and to make amendments to the form in several places. In practice it may be simpler to use a form such as IC05, which allows for sectional completion.

Commencement by the contractor

4.3 MW05 does not refer to the contractor being given 'possession' of the site, but states simply that 'the Works may be commenced' on the date stated in the contract. Such wording is a realistic reflection of what much small work entails, particularly where work may have to be adjusted because the employer expects to be in part occupancy during building operations. It would be implied, however, that the contractor should be given such access as is necessary to complete the Works within the contract period, and failure to do so would constitute a reason beyond its control, thus entitling the contractor to an extension of time. If the work is substantially suspended for a period of a month or more, due to failure to allow necessary access, then this would be grounds for determination under clause 6·8·2·2. Failure to give the contractor access, or granting inadequate access only, may also amount to repudiation, and give the contractor the right to treat the contract as at an end, or bring a claim for damages (*Whittal Builders* v *Chester-le-Street DC*). Any restrictions on access or working methods should therefore be clearly stated in the Contract Documents.

4.4 The parties are, of course, always free to renegotiate the terms of any contract. Therefore, if there is a delay in allowing access, the parties may have to agree new dates for commencement and completion, usually with a financial compensation to the contractor.

Whittal Builders Co Ltd v Chester-le-Street District Council (1987) 40 BLR 82

Whittal Builders contracted with the council on JCT63 to carry out modernisation work to 90 dwellings. The Contract Documents did not mention the possibility of phasing but the council gave the contractor possession of the houses in a piecemeal manner. Even though work of this nature was frequently phased, the judge nevertheless found that the employers were in breach of contract for not giving the contractors possession of all 90 dwellings at the start of the contract, and the contractor was entitled to damages.

4.5   It should be noted that clause 2·2 simply states that the Works may be commenced on the stated date. Therefore the contractor would not be in breach of contract if the Works were commenced some time after this date. In practice this might cause the employer problems with respect to security or insurance. If the contractor is required to be responsible for the site from the stated date then suitable provisions would have to be included in the Contract Documents, and an amendment made to the form.

Occupation by the employer

4.6   In the context of MW05 many employers may wish to use or occupy part of the Works during the time that the contractor is on site. If this is the case it should also be made clear in the tender documents, and agreement reached with the contractor over suitable arrangements. This situation may occur, for example, in domestic projects, or refurbishment work to existing buildings. If at all possible the work should be phased so that the contractor has exclusive access to certain parts for pre-agreed periods. The contract administrator may need to take a proactive role in discussing with the employer how this phasing will work prior to the tender documents being sent out. In some cases it will be inevitable that the employer will need access to the site throughout the project, for example where repair work is carried out to the entrance hall or circulation routes in a residential block, and it is not feasible to evacuate the block. Again, the requirements must be made clear in the tender documents, so that the contractor can allow for adequate health and safety measures to be taken, and include any screening or temporary work, etc, in its tender. In all such cases the insurers of the Works or existing buildings should be kept informed.

Progress

4.7   Although MW05 does not contain an express requirement that the contractor should work with due diligence, depending on the circumstances it is normally implied in a construction contract that a contractor will proceed 'regularly and diligently'. The contractor is free to organise its own working methods and sequences of operations, with the important qualification that it must comply with the Health and Safety Plan. Short periods of inactivity would not necessarily constitute a breach of contract; however, failure to proceed regularly and diligently is a ground for determining the contract (cl 6·4·1·2, see para 9.7 below).

4.8   MW05 does not require the contractor to produce a programme, although there would be nothing to prevent such a requirement being included in the specification, as it might be very useful to the contract administrator, particularly when monitoring progress and assessing extensions of time. It might be helpful if the contractor sets out dates by which key information will be needed, although with many small jobs this should not become necessary. The contract administrator should be careful never to 'approve' any programme in such a way that it becomes a contractually binding document against which his or her own performance in providing information will be judged.

4.9   Where a contractor's programme shows a large float period between the contractor's estimated completion date and the date for completion, this should always be queried. For example, if the contractor has tendered to carry out the work in eight months but produces a programme showing estimated completion in six months, then this may be of little assistance for assessing progress and extensions of time. Also, an early completion date could create difficulties for the employer. What would not be acceptable is for the contractor to claim loss and expense on the grounds that it was prevented from achieving an early completion date through delayed information or decisions by the contract administrator. Just because a contractor's programme shows an intention to complete early, there is no implied duty on the employer to enable the contractor to achieve this early completion (*Glenlion Construction* v *The Guinness Trust*).

Glenlion Construction Ltd v The Guinness Trust (1987) 39 BLR 89

The Trust employed Glenlion Construction on JCT63 to carry out works in relation to a residential development at Bromley, Kent. The contract required the contractor to provide a programme. Disputes arose which went to arbitration and several questions of law regarding the contractor's programme were subsequently raised in court. The contractor claimed loss and expense on the ground that it was prevented from economic working and achieving the early completion date shown on its programme because the architect had failed to provide necessary information and instructions at the dates shown. The court decided that Glenlion was entitled to complete before the date for completion and entitled to carry out the Works in a way which would achieve an earlier completion date. However, there was no implied obligation that the employer (or the architect) should perform its obligations so as to enable the contractor to complete by any earlier completion date shown on the programme.

Completion

4.10   Building contracts usually refer to only one completion date for the Works. The significance of having a completion date is that it provides a fixed point from which damages may be payable in the event of non-completion. Generally in construction contracts the damages are 'liquidated', and usually expressed as a rate per week of overrun.

4.11   The contractor is obliged to complete the Works by the completion date, and in general accepts the risk of any events that might prevent completion by this date. The contractor is relieved of this obligation if the employer causes delays or in some way prevents completion. Most contracts contain provisions allowing for the adjustment of the completion date in the event of certain delays caused by the employer, or neutral delaying events. The contract dates can, of course, always be adjusted by agreement between the parties.

4.12   It is sometimes essential that completion is achieved by a particular date and failure would mean that the result is worthless. This is usually expressed as 'time is of the essence'.

Figure 6 Completion and liquidated damages

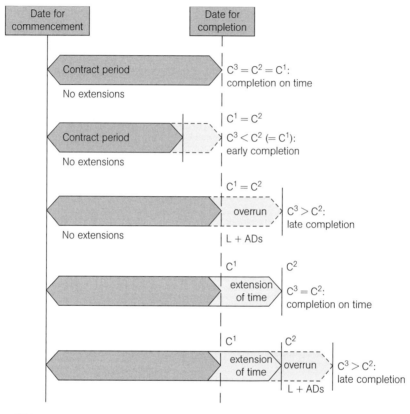

KEY
C1 = Date for completion entered in Contract Particulars
C2 = Date for completion as adjusted by extensions of time
C3 = Practical completion as certified under clause 2·9

Breach of such a term would be considered a fundamental breach, and the employer would be entitled to terminate performance of the contract, and treat all its own obligations as at an end. However, an expression such as 'time is of the essence' is seldom applicable to building contracts, because the inclusion of extensions of time and liquidated damages provisions imply that the parties intended otherwise (*Gibbs* v *Tomlinson*). Nevertheless, there could be occasions where MW05 is used for short-term exhibition or special event constructions, and where failure to meet the date of the event will result in a total loss of the intended benefit to the employer, in which case 'time is of the essence' might be a realistic requirement. In such circumstances the wording of the contract would need amending – always, of course, with the benefit of legal advice.

4.13   MW05 requires an entry in the Contract Particulars (cl 2·2, or 2·3 in MWD05), which gives the date for completion. The contract gives the contract administrator the power to extend time, but makes no provision for reducing the contract period even if substantial work is omitted. The contractor is obliged to complete the Works by this date, or any later date consequent upon an extension of time. If the contractor fails to complete by this date, liquidated damages become payable (*see* Figure 6). Once completion is attained, the Practical Completion Certificate must be issued and the employer is obliged to accept the Works. Employers who wish to accept the Works only on the date in the contract would need to amend the wording.

Gibbs v Tomlinson (1992) 35 ConLR 86

Mr Gibbs employed Tomlinson on the Agreement for Minor Building Works to carry out alterations and construct an extension to his house. Work commenced on site and proceeded satisfactorily until about December 1989 when there were disagreements between the plaintiff and the defendant which resulted in the termination of the contract, and the builder did no work on site after about 12 December 1989. The plaintiff then engaged various workmen to complete the Works, some of whom had previously been employees or sub-contractors of the defendant. He then brought a claim for damages and return of monies allegedly overpaid, claiming that the contractor's failure to complete by the original completion date entitled him to treat the contract as at an end. Mr Recorder Harvey QC found this was not the case, stating that MW80 did not expressly make time of the essence, and that clause 2·3 envisaged that the contractor would continue with the work and pay liquidated damages at the specified rate.

Extensions of time

Principle

4.14   One important reason for an extension of time clause is to preserve the employer's right to liquidated damages in the event that the contractor fails to complete on time, due wholly or in part to some action for which the employer is responsible. If there were no provisions to grant extensions of time, and a delay occurred that was caused at least in part by the employer, this would in effect be a breach of contract by the employer and the contractor would no longer be bound to complete by the completion date (*Peak* v *McKinney*). The employer would therefore lose the right to liquidated damages, even though much of the blame for the delay might rest with the contractor. The phrase 'time at large' is often used to describe this situation. In most cases, however, the contractor would nevertheless remain under obligation to complete within a reasonable time.

Peak Construction (Liverpool) Ltd v McKinney Foundations Ltd (1970) 1 BLR 111 (CA)

Peak Construction were main contractors on a contract to construct a multi-storey block of flats for Liverpool Corporation. The main contract was not on any of the standard forms, but a contract drawn up by the council. McKinney Foundations were nominated sub-contractors to design and construct the piling. After the piling was complete and the sub-contractors had left the site, serious defects were discovered in one of the piles, and following further investigation minor defects were found in several other piles. Work was halted while the best strategy for remedial work was debated between the parties. The city surveyor did not accept the initial remedial proposals, and it was agreed that an independent engineer would prepare a proposal, but the council delayed making the appointment. Altogether it was 58 weeks before work resumed, although the remedial work took only 6 weeks, and the main contractors brought a claim against the sub-contractors for damages.

The Official Referee at first instance found that the entire 58 weeks was delay caused by the nominated sub-contractor and awarded £40,000 damages for breach of contract, based in part on liquidated damages, which the corporation had claimed from the contractor. McKinney appealed, and the Court of Appeal found that the 58 weeks could not possibly be all due to the breach of the sub-contractor, but was in part caused by the tardiness of the Corporation. This being the case, and as there were no provisions in the contract for extending time for their delay, the Corporation lost their right to claim liquidated damages, and this component of the damages awarded against the sub-contractor was disallowed.

Procedure

4.15   Under MW05 the contractor must give written notice to the contract administrator, 'if it becomes apparent that the Works will not be completed by the Date for Completion . . . for reasons beyond the control of the Contractor' (cl 2·7, or 2·8 in MWD05).

4.16   This obligation is quite limited, in that notice only has to be given if completion is likely to be delayed (i.e. not simply if there is a delay in progress), and even then only if the delay is caused by reasons beyond the contractor's control. This limitation could cause problems in practice. It is often important that the contract administrator should be made aware as soon as possible of any difficulty over meeting the completion date, in order to keep the employer informed, and so that measures which might mitigate the problem can be considered. If it is anticipated that such notification is essential, then this should be made clear in the tender documents, and a suitable amendment made to the form.

4.17   It is suggested that the phrase 'so notify' suggests that the contractor should set out the causes in the written notice. In any case for practical purposes the contractor should give as much information as possible about the causes and the extent, in order that the contract administrator may assess what extension might be appropriate.

4.18   Once notice has been given, the contract administrator is required to make 'such extension of time for completion as may be reasonable' (cl 2·7, or 2·8 in MWD05). Although the clause is not very clearly worded, it appears to be stating that the contract administrator must grant an extension of time if the completion date is delayed for reasons beyond the contractor's control, but that the size of the extension is to be assessed on a reasonable basis.

4.19   For guidance on what might be considered to be beyond the contractor's control, the contract administrator might have regard to those matters listed as 'Relevant Events' under SBC05, for example exceptional and adverse weather, the 'Specified Perils', strikes, failure to supply information, site access and indeed any difficulty in movement on or around site. The phrase is, however, broadly expressed and might not be limited to those events. On the other hand, the contractor could be assumed to have allowed for any circumstances which had been explained clearly in the tender documentation, for example access restrictions, even though these may in practice be beyond its control. If the nature

Figure 7 The MW05 timeline

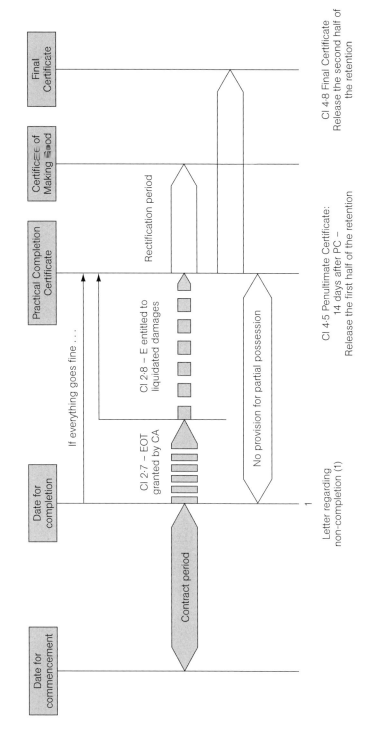

KEY:
1: Under MW05 Non-completion Certificate not required
EOT: Extension of time
E: Employer
CA: Contract Administrator

and extent of the restrictions have been made clear then they are unlikely to entitle the contractor to an extension of time.

4.20   It is also suggested that the contractor might be expected to have allowed for any circumstances which a competent contractor could have predicted, for example the occurrence of bad (but not unusually bad) weather in January. However, this is a difficult point as it would rely on the courts implying a term that things which could be predicted are within the contractor's control. This was not the approach taken by the court in *Scott Lithgow* v *Secretary of State for Defence*, where the court preferred to give the phrase its ordinary meaning.

Scott Lithgow Ltd v Secretary of State for Defence (1989) 45 BLR 1 (HL)

Scott Lithgow Ltd were the successors to Scott's Shipbuilding Co (1969) Ltd which contracted with the Ministry of Defence to construct two 'Oberon' class submarines. The contract required that pressure-tight cables should be supplied by certain firms. One of these firms, BICC, became sub-contractors for the supply of the cables. The cables were found to be defective and had to be replaced. Scott Lithgow brought proceedings against BICC, which were settled for a sum less than the losses suffered through having to replace the cables. Scott Lithgow then gave notice of arbitration under the main contract.

A case was then stated to the Inner House of the Court of Session, and certain points appealed to the House of Lords. Clause 20A·3 of the contract had stated that the contractor should be paid for the effect of 'exceptional dislocation and delay arising during the construction of the vessel due to alterations, suspension of work, or any other cause beyond the contractor's control'. The House of Lords held that failure by suppliers or sub-contractors in breach of their contractual duties to Scott Lithgow were not matters which, according to the ordinary use of language, could be regarded as within Scott Lithgow's control. Lord Keith of Kinkel pointed out that whether or not the failure of the cables had been a matter within the control of Scott Lithgow was a question of fact. The contractor's position depends on demonstrating that 'he has no means of securing that (his requirements) are met. If the contractor failed to stipulate a time for delivery, consequent delay would be his own responsibility but if he did so stipulate and delivery was late the position would be different' (at page 13).

4.21   MW05 makes it clear that default of sub-contractors or suppliers is a reason within the control of the contractor (cl 2·7, or 2·8 in MWD05). It is suggested that the wording of this is clear enough to include even default by sub-contractors or suppliers named by the contract administrator in the specification.

4.22   There are no time limits on when the contract administrator must respond to the contractor's notice, but it is suggested that this should be done as soon as possible, in order to preserve the employer's right to liquidated damages. The contract administrator should either fix a new completion date or notify the contractor that no extension of time is due. The contract administrator might call for information if this is necessary to make a fair and reasonable assessment, but this must never be regarded as a delaying tactic. The contract does not appear to prevent the contract administrator later awarding an additional extension, if this seems reasonable in the light of further information.

4.23   The right of the contract administrator to award an extension of time is limited in several important respects. First, it appears to be dependent on the contractor having given notice, and it is even arguable that the notice should be given before the date for completion. This will present the contract administrator with a dilemma in the unlikely event that the contractor fails to submit a notice where the employer has caused delay, or submits the notice late. The right to deduct liquidated damages may be jeopardised if the contract administrator is unable to extend the contract period. The best policy may be to award an extension in any case, allowing the contractor to take the matter to adjudication if it chooses. It would seem unlikely that a court would find that the parties had intended that absence or lateness of notice should have such a drastic effect (*Terry Pincott* v *Fur & Textile Care*).

Terry Pincott v Fur & Textile Care Ltd (1986) 3-CLD-05-14

Fur & Textile Care, a dry cleaning business, appointed architect David Daw in relation to an extension to their premises. Terry Pincott was engaged as contractor on the Minor Works Agreement. A Certificate of Practical Completion was issued on 13 August 1982. The contractor then submitted a request for an extension of time of 16 weeks on 8 September, which the architect granted in full on 14 September. HH Judge Smout QC stated that 'The request did not accord with the terms of clause 6(ii) of the Minor Works Agreement in that [the contractor] did not notify [the architect] prior to the anticipated date for completion. I doubt, however, whether time is of the essence in regard to that sub-clause'. The lateness of itself would probably not have invalidated the extension, but the architect in this case failed to exercise independent professional judgement in awarding it. The extension was therefore not a bona fide exercise of his powers and was invalid.

4.24   The second limitation is that there appear to be no provisions whereby the contract administrator may reduce a previous extension of time by fixing an earlier completion date where work has been omitted. Nevertheless, it is suggested that if work has been omitted, the contract administrator could take this into account when deciding what might be a reasonable extension in response to some further notice by the contractor.

4.25   The third limitation is that there appear to be no provisions whereby the contract administrator may award further extensions of time in respect of delaying events which occur after the date for completion or any extended completion date, i.e. when the contractor is in 'culpable delay'. The use of the phrase 'will not be completed by' suggests that clause 2·7 (cl 2·8 in MWD05) is referring only to events before the date for completion. The court in *Balfour Beatty* v *Chestermont Properties* concluded that the contract administrator had no such power, but this was in the context of a form that made express provision for a 'review' of extensions of time. There is no such review provision in MW05, so it may be that it would be viewed differently, but cases in the past indicate that courts take a strict approach to implying terms which extend the employer's rights in regard to extending time. The best approach may be for the employer to agree a revised completion date with the contractor, who in practice is unlikely to object as there would be little to be gained. Nevertheless this emphasises the importance of dealing with all extension of time applications promptly.

Balfour Beatty Building Ltd v Chestermont Properties Ltd (1993) 62 BLR 1

In a contract on JCT80 the Works were not completed by the revised completion date and the architect issued a Non-Completion Certificate. The architect then issued a series of variation instructions and a further extension of time, which had the effect of fixing a completion date two and a half months before the first of the variation instructions. He then issued a further Non-Completion Certificate and the employer proceeded to deduct liquidated damages. The contractor took the matter to arbitration and then appealed certain decisions on preliminary questions given by the arbitrator. The court held that the architect's power to grant an extension of time pursuant to clause 25·3·1·1 (similar to clause 2·7 in MW05) could only operate in respect of Relevant Events that occurred before the original or the previously fixed completion date, but the power to grant an extension under clause 25·3·3 applied to any Relevant Event.

Assessment

4.26   It is an obligation on the contract administrator to issue extensions of time when properly due and any failure on the part of the contract administrator to do so is a breach on the part of the employer. In every case the contract administrator should assess the effect of the delay on the contract completion date. A contractor's programme could be useful as a guide but would not be binding. The effect on progress is assessed in relation to the work being carried out at the time of the delaying event, rather than the work that was programmed to be carried out. The contract does not set this out, but it is suggested that it would be implied that the contractor should take reasonable steps to prevent delay, although not to the extent of incurring excessive expenditure. The contract administrator is not required to give reasons as to why a particular extension was awarded. However, it would be prudent to make careful records in case the matter is taken to adjudication.

4.27   The effects of any delay on completion are not always easy to predict. Nevertheless, the contract administrator is required to reach an opinion, and in doing this owes a duty to both parties to be fair and reasonable (*Sutcliffe* v *Thackrah*). This applies even where the delay may have been caused by the contract administrator, for example where he or she has failed to issue information in sufficient time.

4.28   It sometimes happens that two or more delaying events occur simultaneously, or with some overlap, and this can raise difficult questions with respect to the awarding of extensions of time. In the case of concurrent delays involving two or more causes, it has been customary to grant the extension in respect of the dominant reason, but this is only appropriate where the dominant reason begins before, and ends after, any other reasons.

4.29   Where one overlapping delaying event is beyond the control of the contractor and the other is not, in other words one is the employer's risk and the other the contractor's, a difficult question arises as to what extension of time is due. It would seem logical that the contractor should be given an extension of time for the full length of delay caused by the reason beyond the control of the contractor, irrespective of the fact that during the overlap the contractor was also causing delay. Taking any other approach, by, for example, splitting the overlap period and awarding only half to the contractor, could result in the untenable position of the contractor being subject to liquidated damages for delay partly caused by the employer.

Occupation before practical completion

4.30   MW05 makes no provision for the employer to use or occupy the site or the Works or any part prior to practical completion. If arrangements for phased occupation have not been agreed in the Contract Documents, there may arise a situation where the contractor has not completed by the date for completion but where part of the Works are complete or sufficiently complete to allow the employer to have beneficial use of those parts, and the employer is anxious to occupy them. There is nothing in the contract that allows for this; therefore a separate 'ad hoc' agreement would have to be made.

4.31   An interesting suggestion was put forward in the 'Practice' section of the *RIBA Journal* (February 1992) (see Figure 8). Although not directed at MW05, it could be adapted to

Figure 8 Practice Section, *RIBA Journal*

Employer's possession before practical completion under JCT contracts
It is not uncommon for the Employer, after the completion date has passed, to wish to take possession of the Works before the contractor has achieved practical completion. In this event an ad hoc agreement between employer and contractor is required to deal with the situation. In respect of such an agreement, members may wish to have regard to the following note . . .

Outstanding items
Where it is known to the architect that there are outstanding items, practical completion should not be certified without specially agreed arrangements between the employer and the contractor. For example, in the case of a contract where the contract completion date has passed it could be so agreed that the incomplete building will be taken over for occupation, subject to postponing the release of retention and the beginning of the defects liability period until the outstanding items referred to in a list to be prepared are completed, but relieving the contractor from liability for liquidated damages for delay as from the date of occupation, and making any necessary changes in the insurance arrangements. In such circumstances either the certificate of practical completion form should not be used or it should be altered to state or refer to the specially agreed arrangements. In making such arrangements the architect should have the authority of the client-employer.

When the Employer is pressing for premature practical completion there is a need to be particularly careful where there are others who are entitled to rely on the issue of a practical completion certificate and its consequences. In the case where part only of the Works is ready for hand-over the partial possession provisions can be operated to enable the employer with the consent of the contractor to take possession of the completed part.

suit this contract. In this arrangement, in return for being allowed to occupy the premises, the employer agrees not to claim liquidated damages during the period of occupation, or to claim it at a reduced rate. Practical completion obviously cannot be certified, and there is no release of retention money until it is. Matters of insuring the Works will need to be settled with the insurers. Because such an arrangement would be outside the terms of the contract it should be covered by a properly drafted agreement which is signed by both parties. It may also be sensible to agree that in the event that the contractor still fails to achieve practical completion by the end of an agreed period, the rate of liquidated damages would then increase. In most circumstances this arrangement would be of benefit to both parties, and is far preferable to issuing a heavily qualified certificate of practical completion listing 'except for' items.

Practical completion

4.32   Under clause 2·9 (2·10 in MWD05) the contract administrator is obliged to certify the date at which, in the contract administrator's opinion, Works have reached practical completion and the contractor has complied sufficiently with clause 3·9·3 (supply of information required for the Health and Safety File). The date certified is the date when the last condition is fulfilled: in other words, if there is a delay before receiving the health and safety information, the date of its receipt should be the date on the certificate, irrespective of the fact that practical completion of the Works was achieved days or even weeks earlier. The use of the term 'sufficiently complied' may allow the contract administrator to use his or her discretion in issuing the certificate with some information missing. The contract administrator should, however, be very careful not to place the employer in a position where it would be in breach of the CDM Regulations.

4.33   Unfortunately, the drafting of the contract is not as consistent as it might be in relation to practical completion. It refers in several clauses to 'the date of practical completion' rather than the date certified under clause 2·9. As clause 2·9 refers to practical completion of the Works and the provision of CDM information as two separate events, both of which have to have occurred for the certificate to be issued, there is at least room for argument that where other clauses refer to 'the date of practical completion' they are referring to the first event only.

4.34   For example, in clause 2·8 liability for liquidated damages is stated to run until the 'date of practical completion', and a contractor may try to argue that it should cease once the Works have reached practical completion. It is suggested that the correct interpretation is that the liability runs until the date certified under clause 2·9, regardless of when the Works reach practical completion, not least because the employer may well be in breach of its statutory obligations until the necessary information is provided. The ambiguity in the drafting arises from the failure of the JCT to adjust related clauses after the reference to clause 3·9·3 (Health and Safety File) was added to clause 2·9.

Practical completion of the Works

4.35   Deciding when the Works have reached practical completion often causes the contract administrator some problems. As with other decisions under the contract, it is implied that it will be a fair and reasonable exercise of professional judgement. The contract administrator should be satisfied that there are no patent defects, that all construction work as defined in the contract has been completed; and that if the CDM Regulations apply in full, the contractor has sufficiently complied with obligations in respect of the Health and Safety File. However, it has been held that the contract administrator has a discretion to certify practical completion where there are very minor items of work left incomplete, on 'de minimus' principles (*H. W. Neville (Sunblest)* v *William Press*).

H. W. Neville (Sunblest) Ltd v William Press & Son Ltd (1981) 20 BLR 78

William Press entered into a contract with Sunblest to carry out foundations, groundworks and drainage for a new bakery on a JCT63 contract. A Practical Completion Certificate was issued, and new contractors commenced a separate contract to construct the bakery. A Certificate of Making Good defects and a final certificate were then issued for the first contract, following which it was discovered that the drains and the hard standing were defective. William Press returned to the site and remedied the defects, but the second contract was delayed by four weeks and Sunblest suffered damages as a result. It commenced proceedings, claiming that William Press was in breach of contract and in its defence William Press argued that the plaintiff was precluded from bringing the claim by the conclusive effect of the final certificate.

Judge Newey decided that the final certificate did not act as a bar to claims for consequential loss. In reaching this decision he considered the meaning and effect of the Certificate of Practical Completion and stated:

> I think that the word 'practically' in clause 15(1) gave the architect a discretion to certify that William Press had fulfilled its obligation under clause 21(1) where very minor de-minimus work had not been carried out, but that if there were any patent defects in what William Press had done then the architect could not have issued a Certificate of Practical Completion (at page 87).

4.36   However, such discretion should be exercised with extreme caution. It should not extend to the issue of a certificate qualified by 'except for the following items' followed by a long list. The rectification period will commence, the contractor may feel little incentive to return, particularly if the retention money held hardly justifies the cost, and the client is likely to take an exaggerated view of what defects remain. It may be worth reminding any employer that is pressing for a Certificate of Practical Completion of the consequences of such action.

4.37   A key consequence is that half of the retention is released, which leaves a retention of only 2.5 per cent (or half of the percentage stated in the Contract Particulars) in hand (cl 4·5). The money may be used to remedy work which the contractor refuses to correct, but is only intended to cover the risk of latent defects, and may not be enough to cover defects which are apparent at practical completion.

4.38   In addition, the rectification period begins at practical completion (cl 2·10). Any work which is completed during the rectification period will not have the benefit of the full period to allow latent defects to emerge. This may be particularly important with respect to services, which require a seasonal cycle to be properly tested: The employer takes over responsibility for the site, and (unless clause 5·4B applies) the contractor will no longer cover the insurance of the Works. The insurers will therefore need to be informed about the programme for the outstanding works: The contractor's liability for liquidated damages ends (cl 2·8·1) so if the employer suffers further losses due to the contractor having to return to site it may find these very difficult to recover: The employer will be the 'occupier' for the purposes of the Occupiers Liability Act and also may be subject to claims regarding health and safety.

Procedure at practical completion

4.39   The contract sets out no procedure for dealing with practical completion, it simply requires the contract administrator to certify it. The Contract Documents may set out a procedure, but the contract administrator should check carefully at tender stage to ensure that the procedure is satisfactory.

4.40   Leading up to practical completion it appears to be widespread practice for contract administrators to issue 'snagging' lists, sometimes in great detail and on a room-by-room basis. The contract does not require this, and neither do most standard terms of appointment. Under the contract, responsibility for quality control and snagging rests entirely with the contractor. In adopting the practice of 'snagging' the contract administrator might be helping the contractor and, although this may appear to benefit the employer, it can create confusion over the liability position, which could cause problems at a future date.

4.41   It is frequently the practice for the contractor to arrange a 'handover' meeting. The term is not used in MW05 and although handover meetings can be of use, particularly in introducing the finished project to the employer, it is better to avoid complex or inflexible procedures in the Contract Documents. Where a handover meeting has been arranged, or the contractor has stated in writing the Works are complete, it still remains the contract administrator's responsibility to decide whether practical completion has been achieved. If he or she feels that the Works are not complete there is no obligation to justify this opinion with schedules of outstanding items. The best course may just be to draw attention to typical items, but to make it clear that any list is indicative and not comprehensive.

4.42   The contract does not set out any time limits or procedure for the issue of the certificate, but it would be reasonable to issue the certificate as soon as the criteria in clause 2·9 are met. The certificate is usually sent to the employer, with a copy to the contractor.

Failure to complete by the completion date

4.43   In the event of failure to complete, the employer, provided that it has issued the necessary notice, may deduct damages from the amount due under the next certificate, or reclaim the sum as a debt (cl 2·8·2, or 2·9·2 in MWD05). Note that fluctuations in relation to contribution, levy and tax changes are frozen from this point. Under MW05 the contract administrator is not required to certify non-completion, but it may be prudent to record the failure in a letter to both the employer and the contractor. Once the date for completion has passed, the contractor is said to be in 'culpable delay'.

Liquidated and ascertained damages

4.44   The agreed rate for liquidated and ascertained damages is entered in the Contract Particulars (cl 2·8 or 2·9). This is normally expressed as a specific sum per week (or other period) of delay, to be allowed by the contractor in the event of failure to complete by the completion date. The amount must be calculated on the basis of a genuine pre-estimate of the loss likely to be suffered. Provided that it is, the sum will be recoverable without the need to prove the actual loss suffered, and irrespective of whether the actual loss is significantly less or more than the recoverable sum (*BFI Group of Companies* v *DCB integration Systems*). In other words, once the rate has been agreed, both parties are bound by it. If 'nil' is inserted then this may preclude the employer from claiming any damages at all (*Temloc* v *Errill*), whereas if the clause is left blank the employer may still be able to claim general damages.

BFI Group of Companies Ltd v DCB Integration Systems Ltd [1987] 1 CILL 348

BFI employed DCB on the Agreement for Minor Building Works to refurbish and alter offices and workshops at their transport depot. BFI were given possession of the building on the extended date for completion, but two of the six vehicle bays could not be used for another six weeks as the roller shutters had not yet been installed. Disputes arose which were taken to arbitration. The arbitrator found that the delay in completing the two bays did not cause BFI any loss of revenue, and that BFI were therefore not entitled to any of the liquidated damages. BFI were given leave to appeal to the High Court. HH Judge John Davies QC found that BFI were entitled to liquidated damages. It was quite irrelevant to consider whether in fact there was any loss. Liquidated damages do not run until possession is given to the employer but until practical completion is achieved, which may not be at the same time. Therefore the fact that the employer had use of the building was also not relevant.

Temloc Ltd v Errill Properties (1987) 39 BLR 30 (CA)

Temloc entered into a contract with Errill Properties to construct a development near Plymouth. The contract was on JCT80 and was in the value of £840,000. '£Nil' was entered in the appendix against clause 24·2, liquidated and ascertained damages. Practical completion was certified around six weeks later than the revised date for completion. Temloc brought a claim against Errill Properties for non-payment of some certified amounts and Errill counter-claimed damages for late completion. It was held by the court that the effect of '£Nil' was not that the clause should be disregarded (because, for example, it indicated that it had not been possible to assess a rate in advance), but that it had been agreed that there should be no damages for late completion. Clause 24 is an exhaustive remedy and covers all losses normally attributable to a failure to complete on time. The defendant could not therefore fall back on the common law remedy of general damages for breach of contract.

4.45   The liquidated damages may either be recovered from the contractor as a debt or deducted from monies due (cl 2·8·2, or 2·9·2 in MW05). In both cases the following preconditions must have been met:

• the contractor must have failed to complete the Works by the completion date;

• the contract administrator must have fulfilled all duties with respect to the award of extensions of time.

4.46   MW05 incorporates the requirements of section 111 of the Housing Grants, Construction and Regeneration Act 1996 and if the employer wishes to deduct liquidated damages from an amount payable on a certificate, clause 2·8·2 states that the employer must give a notice pursuant to clause 4·6·2 or 4·8·3. The notice must be reasonably clear but there is no need for a great deal of detail (*Finnegan* v *Community Housing Association*). In addition, if the employer wishes to deduct the damages from the sum due under the Final Certificate, this must have been made clear in writing before the date of the final certificate (cl 2·8·3). This is an earlier notification than that required under clause 4·8·3.

J. F. Finnegan Ltd v Community Housing Association Ltd (1995) 77 BLR 22 (CA)

Finnegan were employed on JCT80 by the Housing Association to build 18 flats at Coram Street, West London. The contractor failed to complete the work on time, and the architect issued a Certificate of Non-Completion. Following the Certificate of Practical Completion an Interim Certificate was issued. The employer sent a notice at the same time as the cheque honouring the certificate, which gave minimal information (i.e. not indicating how LADs had been calculated).

The Court of Appeal considered this sufficient to satisfy the requirement for the employer's written notice in clause 24·2·1. Peter Gibson LJ stated (at page 33): 'I consider that there are only two matters which must be contained in the written requirement. One is whether the employer is claiming a payment or a deduction in respect of LADs. The other is whether the requirement relates to the whole or a part (and, if so, what part) of the sum for the LADs.' He then stated (at page 35): 'I would be reluctant to import into this commercial agreement technical requirements which may be desirable but which are not required by the language of the clause and are not absolutely necessary'. The requirements as to notices have now changed. However, there appears to be no reason why the general comments would not still apply, i.e. that the amount of information required would be no more than the minimum set out in the contractual provisions.

4.47   If an extension of time is given following the date for completion the employer must immediately repay any liquidated damages recovered for the period up to the new completion date. In *Department of Environment for Northern Ireland* v *Farrans*, in a case relating to JCT63, it was decided that the contractor has the right to interest on any re-paid liquidated damages. This decision was criticised at the time (see the commentary in volume 19 of the *Building Law Reports*) and would be unlikely to be applied in relation to SBC05 where the wording is now different. However, as the wording in MW05 is similar to that in JCT63, the right to interest in relation to this form remains an open question.

Department of Environment for Northern Ireland v Farrans (Construction) Ltd (1981) 19 BLR 1 (NI)

Farrans was employed to build an office block under JCT63. The original date for completion was 24 May 1975, but this was subsequently extended to 3 November 1977. During the course of the contract, the contract administrator issued four Certificates of Non-Completion. By 18 July 1977 the employer had deducted £197,000 in liquidated damages, but following the second Non-Completion Certificate re-paid £77,900 of those deductions. This process was repeated following the issue of the subsequent Non-Completion Certificates. Farrans brought proceedings in the High Court of Justice in Northern Ireland, claiming interest on the sums that had been subsequently re-paid. The court found for the contractor, stating that the employer had been in breach of contract in deducting monies on the basis of the first, second and third certificates, and that the contractor was entitled to interest as a result.

4.48   Certificates should always show the full amount due to the contractor. As explained in the Guidance Note to the form, it is the employer alone that makes the deduction of liquidated damages. The employer should be advised on the completion date (as last revised), the fact of failure to complete by the date, the date of practical completion, and reminded of its right to deduct the damages and the procedure that must be followed. The employer would not be considered to have waived its claim by a failure to deduct damages from the first or any certificate under which this could validly be done, and would always be able to deduct the amount from a later certificate, or to reclaim it as a debt at any point up until the final certificate.

5   Control of the Works

5.1   The contract administrator derives authority solely from the wording of the contract and will, for example, supply necessary information, issue instructions and issue certificates or notices. In some matters the contract administrator will act as agent of the employer, for example when issuing instructions which vary the Works, and in others will act as independent decision maker, for example when issuing certificates or deciding on claims for an extension of time. Failure to comply with any obligation (usually prefaced by the phrase 'the contract administrator shall') will constitute failure on the part of the employer tantamount to breach of contract (*see* Figures 9 and 10).

5.2   Carrying out of the contract works, including the manner in which the Works are undertaken, is solely the responsibility of the main contractor. The duty of the contract administrator to the employer will normally be to inspect the work at intervals (for a useful discussion of this duty see *McGlinn v Waltham Contractors Ltd*). The obligation and purpose of such visits will arise directly from the terms of the professional appointment as agreed with the employer, and of course MW05 includes no express provision relating to inspection or monitoring of work by the contract administrator. Clearly, when he or she is required under the contract to form an opinion on various matters, including the standard of work and materials prior to issuing a certificate, then it would be implied, even if not expressly set out in the terms of appointment, that some form of inspection must take place.

Figure 9 Key powers of the contract administrator

Clause	Contract administrator's express power
2·5·1	Express satisfaction with contractor's proposal to deal with inconsistency in CDP documents
2·10/2·11	Instruct that defects can remain
3·3·1	Consent to domestic sub-contractors
3·4	Issue written instructions to the contractor
3·6·1	Instruct variations, including additions to or omissions from the Works and the order or period in which they are to be carried out
3·6·2	Agree the price of variations with the contractor before they are carried out
3·8	Exclude employed persons from the site
6·4·1	Give the contractor notice of defaults

Contractor's representative

5.3   The contractor is required to keep a competent 'person-in-charge' (cl 3·2) on the site at all reasonable times to receive any instructions given by the contract administrator, and to act as the contractor's agent on site. Although there is no requirement in the contract

Figure 10 Key duties of the contract administrator

Clause	Contract administrator's duty
2·3/2·4	Issue any further information necessary
2·3/2·5	Issue all certificates
2·5·1	Correct inconsistencies between Contract Documents
2·7/2·8	Make in writing such extensions of time as may be reasonable
2·9/2·10	Certify practical completion
2·10/2·11	Notify contractor of defects
2·11/2·12	Certify that defects have been made good
3·4·1	Confirm instructions in writing
3·6·2	Endeavour to agree value of variation with contractor
3·6·3	Value variation instructions
3·6·3	Ascertain amount of direct loss and/or expense
3·7	Issue instructions regarding expenditure of provisional sums
4·3·1	Certify progress payments
4·5	Issue penultimate certificate
4·8·1	Issue final certificate
5·4A·3	Issue certificates regarding insurance monies to be paid to the contractor
5·4B·2	Issue instructions regarding reinstatement and making good of loss or damage

conditions to have the person named, it would be sensible to set this requirement out in the specification, or alternatively ask for the name and expected duration on site to be minuted at a pre-contract meeting. In extreme cases the contract administrator has the power to exclude persons from the Works (cl 3·8), but this is only likely to be used where an employee may be seriously affecting operations on site.

Clerk of works

5.4   There is no provision in MW05 for an independent clerk of works. If a clerk of works is to be engaged by the employer then this would have to be made clear at tender stage, and suitable provisions would have to be agreed regarding access and facilities.

CDM co-ordinator

5.5   It is the employer's obligation under the contract to ensure that the CDM co-ordinator carries out all the relevant duties under the CDM Regulations (cl 3·9·1). It is the contractor's responsibility to develop the Construction Phase Plan so that it complies with the Regulations, and to ensure that the Works are carried out in accordance with the Plan. The CDM co-ordinator will monitor the development of the Plan, but has no duty to inspect the Works and would be very unlikely to visit the site unless there is some very unusual circumstance, such as the discovery of an unanticipated hazard. The main responsibility for ensuring that correct health and safety measures are employed on site rests with the contractor.

Information to be provided by the contract administrator

5.6   MW05 accepts that the Contract Documents might not contain sufficient information to enable the project to be constructed. Even if the Works have been fully specified it is likely, for example, that information regarding assembly, location, detail dimensions, colours, etc will be needed by the contractor during construction. Supply of this further information will usually form part of the contract administrator's duties to the employer under the terms of appointment.

5.7   MW05 refers to the contract administrator's obligation to provide 'any further information necessary for the proper carrying out of the Works' (cl 2·3). This obligation is repeated in the MWD05 version (cl 2·4), although it is suggested it does not extend to providing information relating to the Contractor's Designed Portion, except where there is an inconsistency or ambiguity in the Employer's Requirements. The forms do not require the information to be released under a 'contract administrator's instruction', but this is sound practice, as it would enable the clause 3·4 provisions to be brought into operation if necessary (see para 5.11 below). If any of the information supplied introduces changes or additions to the Works it should certainly be covered by a contract administrator's instruction requiring a variation.

5.8   The contract sets out no time limits in regard to the provisions of information. However, in order to avoid causing delay, it would be wise to recognise that information and instructions should be provided in sufficient time to allow the contractor to complete by the completion date, or, if the contractor appears unlikely to complete by this date, at a date when it is reasonably necessary for the contractor to receive the information.

5.9   Under MW05 there is no requirement for the contractor to advise the contract administrator of when information may be needed. It might, therefore, be prudent to set up a procedure (possibly at site meetings) where the contractor is requested to list the information that may be needed, and when.

Information provided by the contractor

5.10   The contractor as 'Principal Contractor' may be required by the Planning Supervisor to provide information in relation to the Health and Safety File (cl 3·9·3). It should be noted, however, that MW05 does not contain express provisions for 'as built' drawings. If these are needed, the specific requirement should be set out in the specification or schedules.

5.11   MWD05 includes limited provisions regarding the supply of information relating to the CDP. The contractor is required to provide the contract administrator with two copies of 'such drawings or details and specification of materials, goods and workmanship and (if requested) required calculations and information, as are reasonably necessary to explain the Contractor's Designed Portion' (cl 2·1·5). The contractor may not commence the related work until after seven days from the date the information is supplied (cl 2·1·6). In practice seven days is little time to consider all the implications of integrating the CDP with the rest of the project, and the administrator will need to act swiftly if the information reveals any potential problems. There are no provisions to deal with any comments he or she might wish to make on the information. Although this does not prevent the contract administrator from commenting, the contractor is not obliged to incorporate the comments. If an agreement cannot be reached on matters raised, the contract administrator may need to instruct a variation to the CDP under clause 3·6·1 (see para 5.12 below).

Contract administrator's instructions

5.12   The contract administrator has the power to issue instructions (cl 3·4). Sometimes the contract states that the contract administrator *may* issue instructions (for example, instructions requiring a variation under clause 3·6·1), but at other times the contract states that the contract administrator *shall* issue instructions (for example instructions requiring reinstatement of damaged work under clause 5·4B). The latter is a contractual obligation and failure by the contract administrator to issue the instruction will constitute a breach of contract by the employer. If the employer gives an instruction other than through the contract administrator this would be of no effect under the contract. The contractor would be under no obligation to comply with any such instruction. If the contractor, however, does carry out the instruction a court might consider that there had been an agreed amendment to the contract, but the consequences would be difficult to sort out in practice and the employer would be very unwise to risk such action.

5.13   Instructions empowered by the contract are:

- acceptance of defective work remains (cl 2·10/2·11);

- changes in the CDP or the Works (Variations) (cl 3·6·1);

- expenditure of provisional sums (cl 3·7);

- exclusion of persons from the Works (cl 3·8);

- reinstatement after damage (cl 5·4B·2·1).

5.14   Clause 3·4 requires the contractor to comply with written instructions 'forthwith'. If any instructions are given orally, the contract administrator must confirm the instruction in writing within two days, otherwise it would be of no effect. As the definition of a day does not exclude weekends (cl 1·4) it would be sensible to confirm all instructions immediately. Although MW05 makes no reference to the contractor confirming oral instructions in writing, the contract administrator would be wise to check any such confirmation and respond. If the contract administrator remains silent he or she may be deemed to have approved the contractor's version. If the contractor carries out work on the basis of an oral instruction only, then it is suggested that the contract administrator could later sanction the instruction at any time prior to the issue of the final certificate, but the contractor would be taking a risk.

5.15 There is no special format required for instructions, but it is often convenient to use the forms published by RIBA Publications. Instructions in site meeting minutes might constitute a written confirmation of an oral instruction if issued by the contract administrator, but are unlikely to do so if issued by the contractor. It would depend on the circumstances whether the minutes were sufficiently clear to fall within the terms of the contract, and it is therefore not good practice to rely on this method.

5.16 The contractor must comply with every instruction provided that it is valid and one which the contract administrator is empowered to issue. The contractor must 'forthwith' comply, which for practical purposes means as soon as is reasonably possible (cl 3·4).

5.17 If the contractor does not comply with a written instruction, the employer may employ and pay others to carry out the work to the extent necessary to give effect to the instruction (cl 3·5). The contract administrator must already have given written notice to the contractor requiring compliance with the instruction, and seven days must have elapsed after the contractor's receipt of the notice before the employer may bring in others. This suggests that some recorded form of delivery is desirable. Careful records should be kept to substantiate the costs claimed and competitive tenders obtained if the circumstances permit. If the contractor believes that a contract administrator's instruction might not be empowered by the contract, or justifies clarification, then its last resort would be to raise the matter in adjudication.

Variations

5.18 The contract administrator's instructions often require variations to the Works. Under common law neither party to a contract has the power to unilaterally alter any of its terms. Therefore, neither the employer nor contract administrator would have the power to require any variations unless the contract provides for this. As it is difficult to define some things exactly in advance, most construction contracts contain provisions allowing the employer to vary the Works to some degree. Changes can arise because of unexpected site problems, or because of design changes wanted by the employer, or because the contract administrator has to change information issued to the contractor.

5.19 Under MW05 the contract administrator has the power to order variations, and the scope of what constitutes a variation is set out in clause 3·6·1. It includes 'an addition to, omission from, or other change in the Works or the order or period in which they are to be carried out'. The power does not extend to altering the nature of the contract, nor can the contract administrator issue variations after practical completion. All variations under clause 3·6·1 may result in an adjustment of the Contract Sum and give rise to a claim for an extension of time and direct loss and/or expense. If the Works are suspended as a consequence, this could also be a ground for determination by the contractor.

5.20   The contract administrator may vary the Works, for example by changing the standard of a material specified, and may add to or omit work, or substitute one type of work for another. Although there is no specific provision in MW05, it seems likely that the contract administrator could order removal of work already carried out. The contract administrator is also empowered to order variations affecting the sequence of work, or period for operations to be carried out. What is less clear is whether he or she may vary access or use of the site, limitations on working space or working hours, or any restrictions already imposed. However, the contractor is unlikely to challenge such an instruction, given that the contractor will be paid for such variations and would be entitled to an extension of time. It would also seem likely that a court would imply such a term, at least in relation to restrictions that might be imposed by a local authority, as otherwise the contract might become unworkable.

5.21   Under MWD05 the contract administrator may also instruct a change to the Employer's Requirements which necessitates an alteration to the design of the CDP Works. This provision is carefully worded, and does not empower the administrator to instruct changes to the CDP direct. Under clause 2·1·2, the contractor will not be responsible for any changes to the requirements. In effect, although the contractor is responsible for the design of the CDP, the employer may not be able to hold the contractor responsible for problems resulting from such variations.

Defective work

5.22   Clause 2·1 states that all materials and workmanship shall be of the standard specified in the Contract Documents. The contract administrator will normally inspect at regular intervals to monitor the standard that is being achieved. If any changes were made in order to raise or lower the standard then this would constitute a variation. When the standard achieved appears to be unsatisfactory it can be all too easy for the contract administrator to become involved in directing the day-to-day activities of the contractor on site, particularly with smaller jobs under a contract such as MW05. Apart from being an enormous burden on the contract administrator, this could confuse the issue of who is ultimately responsible for the Works and must be avoided at all costs. The contract administrator would normally, of course, draw the contractor's attention to areas of defective or poor quality work.

5.23   There are no specific measures set out in the contract to deal with defective work. Clearly the contractor should not be paid for any defective work. If this appears to be insufficient incentive, then the contract administrator may instruct that the work in question is carried out in accordance with the contract. Whilst not adding anything to the contractor's primary obligation, it allows the employer to employ others to carry out the work should the contractor refuse to comply. If the contractor insists that the work was correctly carried out, then this dispute might have to be taken to adjudication. If the contract administrator wishes to have tests carried out, then the cost of these would be borne by the employer unless special provisions have been set out in the Contract Documents, as MW05 has no provision for testing or opening up work.

5.24   It would be possible under the terms of the contract to allow the defective work to remain. This would be inadvisable unless the employer is completely satisfied with the work, or the defect is minor and the delay consequent upon correcting the work appears completely out of proportion to the benefit to be gained. The parties would have to agree on any deduction to be made, as the contract administrator has no power to deduct any amount from the Contract Sum. The contract administrator should strongly advise the employer against accepting any defective work that could later cause technical problems or be a source of irritation. The difficult case of *Ruxley Electronics* v *Forsyth* illustrates that it may not be possible to claim the cost of having the work rebuilt at a later date.

Ruxley Electronics and Construction Ltd v *Forsyth* (1995) 73 BLR 1 (HL)

Mr Forsyth employed Ruxley Electronics to build a swimming pool. The drawings and specification required the pool to be seven foot six inches deep at its deepest point, but the completed pool was only six foot nine inches deep. The contractors brought a claim for their unpaid account, and Mr Forsyth counter-claimed the cost of rebuilding the pool, which would be £21,560. The trial judge found that the shortfall in depth did not decrease the value of the pool and that Mr Forsyth had no intention of building a new pool. He rejected the counter-claim but awarded £2,500 as general damages for loss of pleasure and amenity. Mr Forsyth appealed and the Court of Appeal allowed the appeal and awarded him £21,500. The contractor appealed and the House of Lords restored the original ruling, confirming that the cost of reinstatement is not the only possible measure of damages for defective performance of a building contract and is not the appropriate measure where the expenditure would be out of all proportion to the benefit to be obtained.

Sub-contracted work

5.25 Under clause 3·3·1 the contractor may only sub-contract work with the written consent of the contract administrator. Failure to obtain this would be a default, although the contract sets out no remedy. Clause 3·3·1 states, however, that the contract administrator's permission cannot be unreasonably withheld. It is suggested that permission is required for each instance of sub-letting, rather than agreeing to sub-letting in principle.

5.26 There is no requirement to use a particular form of sub-contract and no standard form of sub-contract is yet published specifically for use with MW05, although the generic JCT short sub-contract would be suitable. Whatever form of domestic sub-contract is used, however, it must include certain conditions. Clause 3·3·2 states the sub-contract must provide that the sub-contractor has a right to interest on late payments by the contractor. It is surprising that the JCT decided to 'step down' such a lengthy and complex provision into the Minor Works form, when its sole purpose is to protect the interests of sub-contractors. It is notable that other SBC05 contract provisions, designed to protect the position of the employer in relation to unfixed goods and materials, have not been stepped down.

5.27 The contract makes no provision for naming or nominating a sub-contractor. It is suggested that if a sub-contractor is named in the tender documents, the contractor will remain entirely responsible for the performance of that sub-contractor. However, difficulties may arise if the sub-contractor were to repudiate its contract. The contract does not include a facility for replacement or substitution and it may well be that the employer would be responsible for finding a replacement. Similarly, there may be problems if a design obligation is sub-contracted to a named specialist under MWD05, and defects emerge in relation to that design. Although by no means certain, it is possible that a court would find the main contractor not liable for the design error. It should also be remembered that there is no JCT employer/specialist warranty for use with MWD05 in the event that the employer wishes to be able to hold the specialist sub-contractor directly liable for this work.

5.28   It would be possible to limit the contractor's choice of a sub-contractor to carry out certain work to any one of three or more firms, in a manner similar to the provisions for naming in SBC05. The National Building Specification MW version contains a suitable specification clause. Sometimes a contract administrator's instruction on the expenditure of a provisional sum is used as an opportunity to instruct the contractor to enter into a sub-contract with a particular firm. The contractor should be made aware of such an intention at the time of tendering, in order to reduce the risk of objections which could prove disruptive.

Work not forming part of the contract/persons engaged by the employer

5.29   There are no provisions whereby the employer may engage persons direct to carry out work that does not form part of the contract, while the contractor is carrying out the Works. In practice although making such arrangements is possible it often results in significant problems, as it is unclear who will be responsible for coordinating the work of the two contractors. If it is necessary, the specification would have to have set out this requirement, giving as much detail as possible about the nature and duration of the work. If the work should differ from the details set out, then this might be grounds for an extension of time and other claims by the contractor. It should be remembered that the indemnities given by the contractor under clause 5 (and therefore the insurances under clause 5) do not extend to persons not employed by the contractor.

Making good defects

5.30   The contractor is required to make good any 'defects, shrinkages or other faults' to the Works which appear during the rectification period (cl 2·10, or 2·11 in MWD05). This is stated in the Contract Particulars to be three months, although a different period can be inserted if required. This may be advisable, particularly where there are mechanical services which need to be tested over a range of outdoor temperatures. The obligation extends to defects resulting from a failure of the contractor to comply with its CDP obligations, but would not include defects that may be due, for example, to errors in the design information supplied to the contractor, or to general wear and tear resulting from occupation by the employer. It is suggested also that although this contract provision is limited to those defects that appear after practical completion, and does not extend to defects that were patent at that time, in practice it would be sensible to allow the contractor the opportunity to remedy any such defects (*William Tomkinson* v *Parochial Church Council of St Michael*). The obligation to return to site is in fact of benefit to the contractor as it carries with it a corollary right to have access to the site to make good its own defaults. If the clause were not present, the employer would have the right to employ another firm and bring a claim for damages against the contractor. The cost to the contractor would almost certainly be greater than carrying out the work itself. Although the right to return to site ceases at the end of the three-month period, the contractor's liability for defective materials or workmanship continues throughout the statutory limitation period.

William Tomkinson & Sons Ltd v Parochial Church Council of St Michael (1990) 6 CLJ 319, 8 CLD-08-05

The Council employed William Tomkinson to carry out repair works to their church caused by the contractor's negligence, on the Agreement for Minor Building Works. During the course of the works £100,000 worth of damage was caused to the church organ and other parts of the structure by rainwater. The architects reported complaints about these defects to the contractors orally, but did not issue a schedule of defects. The Council employed other contractors to remedy the defects prior to the date for practical completion. In examining clause 2·5 Judge Stannard concluded that a written schedule of defects was not necessary and that oral notification was sufficient. He also found that the words 'appear within three months of practical completion' extended to defects which appear before practical completion. The true measure of damages was not the church's outlay in repairing the damage but what it would have cost the contractor if it had been required to undertake the repairs.

5.31   MW05 requires the contract administrator to notify the contractor of the existence of defects, but unlike SBC05 does not state that the administrator must issue a schedule of defects. It is suggested that it would be sufficient for the contract administrator to write to the contractor to inform it that defects had appeared, and of their general nature. The onus would then be on the contractor to identify and make good all defective work. If the contract administrator prefers to issue a schedule, it might be wise to state that it is not intended to be a comprehensive list, and that the contractor should make its own inspection. It would also be sensible to make the employer aware that the contractor must be allowed access, as to prevent this may result in the employer being unable to claim for the costs of remedying the defective work (*see Pearce and High* v *Baxter*).

5.32   If the employer would prefer to accept the defects rather than require them to be corrected, then an appropriate deduction should be negotiated. Care should be taken to establish the full extent of the problem before such a course of action is taken, as it is unlikely that the employer would thereafter be able to claim for consequential problems or further remedial work.

5.33   Once satisfied that the contractor's obligations have been discharged, the contract administrator must issue a certificate to that effect (cl 2·11, or 2·12 in MWD05). The certificate is a precondition to the issue of the final certificate. The contract does not state what should happen in respect of defects that appear after the issue of the certificate but before the issue of the final certificate. It appears, however, that the contractor may no longer have any obligation under clause 2·10 nor any right under the contract, to return to site. It is suggested that in such circumstances there would be two possible courses of action. The first would be to make an agreement with the contractor to rectify the defects before the final certificate is issued. If the contractor refused to do this, an amount could be deducted from the Contract Sum to cover the cost of making good the work, but this might involve some risk to the employer. The second and less risky course would be to have the defective work rectified by another contractor, and deduct the amount paid from the Contract Sum. This would involve a delay to the issue of the final certificate and would probably be disputed by the contractor.

Pearce and High Ltd v John P. Baxter and Mrs A. S. Baxter [1999] 1 BLR 101 (CA)

The Baxters employed Pearce and High on MW80 to carry out certain works at their home in Farringdon. Following practical completion, the architect issued Interim Certificate number 5, which the employer did not pay. The contractor commenced proceedings in Oxford County Court, claiming payment of that certificate and additional sums. The employer in its defence and counter-claim relied on various defects in the work that had been carried out. Although the Defects Liability Period had by that time expired, neither the architect nor the employer had notified the contractor of the defects. The Recorder held that clause 2·5 was a condition precedent to the recovery of damages by the employer, and further stated that it was a condition precedent that the building owner had notified the contractor of patent defects within the Defects Liability Period. The employer appealed and the appeal was allowed. Lord Justice Evans stated that there were no clear express provisions within the contract which prevented the employer bringing a claim for defective work, regardless of whether notification had been given. He went on to state, however, that the contractor would not be liable for the full cost to the employer of remedying the defects, if the contractor had been effectively denied the right to return and remedy the defects itself.

---

6   Sums properly due

6.1   The Contract Sum is entered in Article 2. This is seldom the amount which the job actually costs, and the wording of the contract recognises this by the qualifying reference 'or such other sum as shall become payable'.

6.2   The contract figure sometimes contains provisional sums to cover the cost of work that cannot be accurately described or measured at the time of tendering. Also, almost all jobs will entail some variations as work proceeds, and MW05 provides for dealing with the cost of such variations, and the loss and expense due to disruption which may be caused as a result. The form can take into account fluctuations, limited to the contributions, levy and tax changes, or, if preferred, it can be operated as literally a fixed price contract. VAT is, of course, not included in the Contract Sum.

6.3   As a result the Contract Sum will almost certainly need to be adjusted and amounts properly ascertained by the contract administrator will be added or deducted as appropriate when progress payments are certified.

6.4   Arithmetical errors by the contractor in pricing are not allowed as a cause for adjustment. The contractor has agreed to carry out all the work shown in the Contract Documents for the Contract Sum, and errors or omissions in any detailed pricing breakdown are immaterial. Any inconsistency between the Contract Drawings and other documents must be corrected by a contract administrator's instruction and is treated as if it were a variation, but it is suggested that this would not necessarily result in an increase in the Contract Sum (cl 2·4, or 2·5·1 in MWD05). If the work is clearly shown in some of the documents, but does not appear on others, a court would be likely to ask whether, from the point of view of an objective bystander, it is clear that the parties intended that this work should form part of their agreement. The contract administrator should make a similar objective assessment and, if the answer is no, then the variation will result in an adjustment.

Provisional sums

6.5   If sufficient information cannot be provided at the time of tender to allow the contractor to price that item, then a provisional sum may be included in the tender documents to cover the item. Provisional sums included in the contract specification are not subject to SMM7 Rules. It is nevertheless advisable to give the tenderer as much information as possible regarding the nature and construction of the work, how and where the work fits into the building, the scope and extent of the work and any specific limitations on methods or sequence or timing. The contract administrator must issue instructions regarding all work covered by provisional sums (cl 3·7). The work is then to be valued in accordance with clause 3·6·1.

Valuation of variations

6.6   Clause 3·6·3 makes it clear that valuation of variations is the responsibility of the contract administrator, regardless of whether or not a quantity surveyor is appointed. Work is to be valued 'using where relevant' rates and prices in the priced specification or schedules, or the contractor's schedule of rates. 'Relevant' should be understood in the sense that the variation relates to work of a similar character, carried out under similar conditions. Where the work is not of similar character it should be valued on a fair and reasonable basis. Any direct loss and/or expense incurred is to be taken into account in the valuation (see para 6.8 below).

6.7   Under clause 3·6·2 the contract administrator should endeavour to agree a price with the contractor in advance of the work being carried out. The contract administrator would, however, be acting as agent for the employer, and it would be wise to confirm the price with the employer before agreeing to it. A method similar to the 'Schedule 2 quotation' procedure in SBC05 could be adopted, whereby a quotation is requested which should identify the direct cost of complying with the instruction, the period required for extension to the contract period and any amount necessary to cover direct loss and/or expense. It may not be generally appropriate for contracts under MW05 because of the sums involved and the time factor, but for more significant variations this method would bring certainty of outcome for the parties, as both would be bound by what is agreed. The certainty, however, is likely to be secured only at a price, as the contractor would be under no obligation to relate the quotation to the figures in the Contract Documents. If the quotation is unacceptable, the work could still be instructed and valued in the usual way.

Direct loss and/or expense

6.8   Clause 3·6·3 requires that valuations of variations shall include the amount of any 'direct loss and/or expense'. This is the only instance within MW05 where the contract administrator may make such an award. If the contractor suffers losses not related to a variation, these might have to be referred to adjudication, arbitration or litigation, unless some agreement can be reached. The phrase 'direct loss and/or expense' refers to losses suffered as a result of delay or disruption consequent upon the variation, excluding, of course, the direct cost of carrying out the relevant work. The clause also refers to loss and/or expense incurred due to compliance or non-compliance by the employer with health and safety obligations as set out in clause 3·9. This relates purely to variations, and in theory it is possible to envisage situations where losses are caused to the contractor through the employer's compliance with the Regulations, which do not strictly speaking constitute a variation to the Works. Such losses would have to be dealt with outside the terms of the contract.

6.9   In ascertaining loss and expense the contract administrator must determine what has actually been suffered. The sums awarded can include any loss or expense that has arisen directly as the result of the variation. In assessing the amount of damages the object is to put the contractor back into the position in which it would have been but for the disturbance. The contractor ought to be able to show that it has taken reasonable steps to mitigate its loss.

6.10   The following are items which could be included:

- increased preliminaries;

- overheads;

- loss of profit;

- uneconomic working;

- increases due to inflation; and

- interest or finance charges.

6.11   Prolongation costs such as on-site overheads would normally only be claimable for variations affecting after the date for completion. (For head office overheads, etc, see *McAlpine* v *Property and Land Contractors* below.) Interest may also be recoverable, but only if it can be proved to have been a genuine loss (*F. G. Minter* v *WHTSO*).

Alfred McAlpine Homes North Ltd v Property and Land Contractors Ltd (1995) 76 BLR 59

An appeal arose on a question of law arising out of an arbitrator's award regarding the basis for awarding direct loss and expense with respect to additional overheads and hire of small plant, following an instruction to postpone the Works. The judgement contains useful guidance on the basis for awarding direct loss and expense. To 'ascertain' means to 'find out for certain'. It is not necessary to differentiate whether a head of claim is 'loss' or 'expense'. Regarding overheads, a contractor would normally be entitled to recover as a 'loss' the shortfall in the contribution that the volume of work had been expected to make to the fixed head office overheads, but which, because of a reduction in volume and revenue caused by the prolongation, was not in fact made. The fact that *Emden* or *Hudson* formulae depend on certain assumptions mean that they are frequently inappropriate. The losses on the plant should be the true cost to the contractor, not based on notional or assumed hire charges.

F. G. Minter Ltd v Welsh Health Technical Services Organisation (1980) 13 BLR 1 (CA)

Minter was employed by Welsh Health Technical Services Organisation (WHTSO) under JCT63 to construct the University Hospital of Wales (second phase) Teaching Hospital. During the course of the contract several variations were made, and the progress of the Works was affected due to the lack of necessary drawings and information. The contractor was paid amounts in respect of direct loss and/or expense, but the amounts paid were challenged as insufficient. The amounts had not been certified and paid until long after the losses had been incurred, therefore the amounts should have included an allowance in respect of finance charges or interest. Following arbitration several questions were put to the High Court, including whether Minter was entitled to finance charges in respect of any of the following periods:

(a)   between the loss and/or expense being incurred and the making of a written application for the same;

(b)   during the ascertainment of the amount; and/or

(c)   between the time of such ascertainment and the issue of the certificate including the ascertained amount.

The court answered 'no' to all three questions and Minter appealed. The Court of Appeal decided that the answer was 'yes' to the first question and 'no' to the other two.

6.12   Although the contract does not actually state such a requirement, it would be reasonable to assume that the contractor should provide details and particulars of all items concerned with any loss or expense, otherwise it will be extremely difficult for the contract administrator to assess what amount would be reasonable. If no information is forthcoming the contract administrator should nevertheless try to make a fair and reasonable assessment.

6.13   Formulae such as the *Hudson* or *Emden* are sometimes used to estimate head office overheads and profit, which may be difficult to substantiate. These can only be used where it has been established that there has been a loss of this nature. To do this the contractor must be able to show that, but for the delay, the contractor would have been able to earn the amounts claimed on another contract, for example by producing evidence such as invitations to tender which were declined. Such formulae may be useful where it is difficult to quantify the amount of the alleged loss, provided a check is made that the assumptions on which the formulae are based apply.

6.14   Although direct loss and/or expense is a matter of money, not time, which are quite separate issues, there is often a practical correlation in the case of prolongation. Any general implication, however, that there is a link would be incorrect and in principle disruption claims and delay to progress are independent. An extension of time, for example, is not a condition precedent to the award of direct loss and/or expense (*H. Fairweather & Co v Wandsworth*).

6.15   Applications or claims from the contractor must be dealt with according to the procedures of the contract. Failure to certify an amount properly due will not prevent recovery, and could leave the employer liable in damages for breach of contract (*Croudace v London Borough of Lambeth*).

H. Fairweather & Co Ltd v London Borough of Wandsworth (1987) 39 BLR 106

Fairweather entered into a contract with the London Borough of Wandsworth to erect 478 dwellings. The contract was on JCT63. Pipe Conduits Ltd were nominated sub-contractors for underground heating works. Disputes arose and an arbitrator was appointed who made an interim award. Leave to appeal was given on several questions of law arising out of the award. The arbitrator had found that where a delay occurred which could be ascribed to more than one event the extension should be granted for the dominant reason. The dominant reason was strikes, and the arbitrator had granted an extension of 81 weeks for this reason, and made it clear that this reason did not carry any right for direct loss and/or expense. The court stated that an extension of time was not a condition precedent for an award of direct loss and/or expense, and that the contractor would be entitled to direct loss and/or expense for other events which had contributed to the delay.

Croudace Ltd v The London Borough of Lambeth (1986) 33 BLR 25 (CA)

Croudace entered into an agreement with the London Borough of Lambeth to erect 148 dwelling houses, some shops and a hall. The contract was on JCT63 and the architect was the borough's chief architect and the quantity surveyor was the borough's chief quantity surveyor. The architect delegated his duties to a private firm of architects. Croudace alleged that there had been delays and that they had suffered direct loss and/or expense and sent letters detailing the matters to the architects. In reply the architects told Croudace that they had been instructed by Lambeth that all payments relating to 'loss and expense' had to be approved by the borough. The chief architect of Lambeth then retired and was not immediately replaced. There were considerable delays pending a further appointment and Croudace began legal proceedings. The High Court found that the borough was in breach of contract in failing to take the necessary steps to ensure that the claim was dealt with, and was liable to Croudace for this breach. The Court of Appeal upheld this finding.

Fluctuations

6.16   Depending upon the economic climate it may be to the employer's advantage to ask for literally a 'fixed' or 'guaranteed' price. Rather confusingly, the term 'fixed price' in building contracts usually includes for limited fluctuations, such as tax changes. MW05, however, can be operated literally as a fixed price contract (i.e. the Contract Sum will not change unless variations are instructed). MW05 allows for limited fluctuations only, which will apply unless the appropriate entry is deleted in the Contract Particulars (cl 4·11). These are 'contribution, levy and tax changes' fluctuations, i.e. those which result from the intervention of statute after the 'date of tender', which is defined as ten days before the date of the Agreement. The details of how this operates are set out in Schedule 2. There is an opportunity for entering a 'percentage addition', which is unlikely to be in excess of ten per cent. Clause 4·11 is, however, optional and may be deleted in the Contract Particulars. Footnote 14 suggests that this would be appropriate with contracts of limited duration, which in practice would be any contract less than 12 months. If clause 4·11 is deleted, clause 4·10 operates to make the contract truly 'fixed price'.

6.17   Where a contract includes for fluctuations, in the absence of anything to the contrary, these will be payable for the whole time the contractor is on site even though it fails to complete within the contract period (*Peak Construction (Liverpool) Ltd v McKinney Foundations Ltd*). There is a so-called 'freezing' provision in MW05 Schedule 2: 10.1 but this depends on the text of clause 2 being left unamended, and all written notices under clause 2 having been properly dealt with by the contract administrator (Schedule 2: 10.2.2).

Peak Construction (Liverpool) Ltd v McKinney Foundations Ltd (1970) 1 BLR 111 (CA)

Peak Construction were main contractors on a contract to construct a multi-storey block of flats for Liverpool Corporation. As a result of defective work by nominated sub-contractors McKinney Foundations, work on the main contract was halted for 58 weeks, and the main contractors brought a claim against the sub-contractors for damages. The Official Referee at first instance found that the entire 58 weeks was delay caused by the nominated sub-contractor, and awarded £40,000 of damages, £10,000 of which was for rises in wage rates during the period. McKinney appealed, and the Court of Appeal found that the award of £10,000 could not be upheld as clause 27 of the main contract entitled Peak Construction to claim this from the Corporation right up until the time when the work was halted to make arrangements for payment in good time.

---

7   Certification

7.1   One of the most important duties of the contract administrator under MW05 is to certify sums properly due to the contractor. Whether or not a quantity surveyor is employed, the contract administrator is responsible for both the valuations and for issuing certificates. It is a duty to be exercised with care and skill, and failure in this respect could amount to negligence. On the one hand the contractor depends on cash flow which proper payment should provide, and is entitled to be paid in accordance with the terms of the contract. On the other hand over-valuation and certification could place the employer's interests at risk, should the contractor become bankrupt, perhaps leaving a legacy of faulty workmanship and disputes over the ownership of unfixed materials. The contract administrator's duty to the employer is fairly clear since the case of *Sutcliffe* v *Thackrah* and it seems possible that there is a duty also to the contractor following *Salliss & Co* v *Calil and W. F. Newman & Associates*. This is a difficult area of the law which is constantly developing, and it would be sensible for the contract administrator to proceed on the basis that such a duty of care exists.

Sutcliffe v Thackrah (1974) 4 BLR 16 (CA)

An architect issued certificates on a contract for the construction of a dwelling house. The contractor's employment was determined for proper reasons following which the contractor went bankrupt. It then became apparent that much of the work, which had been included in the Interim Certificates, was defective, and the architect was found negligent. In the House of Lords, when reviewing the role of the architect, Lord Reid stated:

> Many matters may arise in the course of the execution of a building contract where a decision has to be made which will affect the amount of money which the contractor gets . . . the building owner and the contractor make their contract on the understanding that in all such matters the architect will act in a fair and unbiased manner and it must therefore be implied into the owner's contract with the architect that he shall not only exercise due skill and care but also reach such decisions fairly holding the balance between his client and the contractor. (at page 21)

Michael Salliss & Co Ltd v Calil and William F. Newman & Associates (1987) 13 ConLR 69

Calil employed contractor Michael Salliss for some refurbishment works on JCT63. W. F. Newman acted as architect and quantity surveyor under the contract. The contractor commenced proceedings against the employer and joined the architects as second defendants, claiming that the architect was in breach of his duty to use all professional skill and care in granting only a 12-week extension of time when a 29-week extension was due.

There was a sub-trial as to whether the contractor could recover damages against the architect. HH Judge Fox-Andrews held that under a JCT contract the architect owed a duty to the contractor to act fairly between the employer and contractor in matters such as certification and extensions of time. He also noted that: 'in many respects an architect in circumstances such as these owes no duty to the contractors. He owes no duty to contractors in respect of the preparation of plans and specifications or in deciding matters such as whether or not he should cause a survey to be carried out. He owes no duty of care to a contractor whether or not he should order a variation. Once, however, he has ordered a variation he has to act fairly in pricing it' (at page 79). Although this case was followed by another where an engineer was found to have no duty to the contractor (*Pacific Associates Inc v Baxter* (1988) 44 BLR 33 (CA)), in that instance the contract contained a special provision purporting to exempt the engineer from liability.

7.2   The issue of certificates is referred to in clause 4·3, but there is little on the procedures to be adopted. It would be sensible to adopt the usual JCT practice found in other forms, and issue the certificate to the employer with a copy to the contractor at the same time. The procedure to be used should be established at the outset, either by setting it out in the Contract Documents or agreeing it at a pre-contract meeting.

Progress payments

7.3   Payment is to be made by the employer to the contractor after the issue of certificates by the contract administrator (cl 4·3·1). These are to be issued at intervals of four weeks, calculated from the 'Date for Commencement of the Works'. This is the date entered in the Contract Particulars, not necessarily the date when the contractor actually commenced work.

7.4   Unlike some other JCT forms, MW05 makes no provision for advance payment to the main contractor, nor for payment on commencement of the work (in effect the same thing), so if this is required, the contract terms would have to be amended. There is always a risk in making any such payment, and the contract administrator and employer should be quite clear as to what compensatory benefits, such as a reduction in the Contract Sum, would result.

7.5   Under clause 4·3 it is the contract administrator's responsibility to determine the value of the progress payment, even though the task might be delegated to a quantity surveyor. The clause requires that certificates state not only the amount to be paid, but also 'to what the progress payment relates and the basis on which the amount of the progress payment was calculated'. It is unlikely that a great deal of detail will be required here; a short schedule will probably be sufficient. Similar provisions are included for the final certificate.

7.6   Clause 4·3·1 states that progress payments should include the value of the Works properly executed and the value of materials and goods properly on site. There is no provision for the value of off-site materials, goods or prefabricated items. The valuation should, of course, take into account any relevant variations, including any instructions issued under clause 5·4B·2 for reinstatement after fire, etc, and amounts in respect of the fluctuations provisions, if operated (Schedule 2).

Value of work properly executed

7.7 The contract administrator should only certify after having carried out an inspection to a reasonably diligent standard. The contract does not set a date, but normally the certificate should include for work carried out up to seven days before the date of the certificate. Architects should not include any work that appears not to have been properly executed, whether or not it is about to be remedied or the retention is adequate to cover remedial work (*Townsend* v *Stone* and *Sutcliffe* v *Chippendale & Edmondson*). Where work which has been included in a certificate subsequently proves to be defective the value can be omitted from the next certificate. The value of the work will be calculated using the prices and rates shown in specification or schedules, or the contractor's schedule of rates, whichever is appropriate.

Townsend v Stone Toms & Partners (1984) 27 BLR 26 (CA)

Mr Townsend engaged architects Stone Toms in connection with the renovation of a farmhouse in Somerset. John Laing Construction Ltd were employed to carry out the work on JCT67 Fixed Fee Form of Prime Cost Contract. Following the end of the Defects Liability Period the architects issued an Interim Certificate that included the value of work which they had already included in their schedule of defects, and which they knew had not yet been put right. Mr Townsend brought proceedings against both Stone Toms and Laing. The deputy official referee found that the architect was not negligent in issuing the Interim Certificate. Mr Townsend appealed and the Court of Appeal held that the architect had been negligent. Oliver LJ stated:

> The whole purpose of the certification is to protect the client from paying to the builder more than the proper value of the work done, less proper retention, before it is due. If the architect deliberately over-certifies work which he knows has not been done properly, this seems to be a clear breach of his contractual duty, and whether certification is described as 'negligent' or 'deliberate' is immaterial. (at page 46)

Sutcliffe v Chippendale & Edmondson (1971) 18 BLR 149

(Note this case is the first instance decision, which was appealed to the Court of Appeal sub nom *Sutcliffe* v *Thackrah*, discussed above.)

Mr Sutcliffe engaged the architects Chippendale & Edmondson in relation to a project to build a new house. No terms of engagement were agreed, but the architects proceeded to design the house, invite tenders, and arrange for them the appointment of a contractor on JCT63. Work progressed slowly and towards the end of the work it became obvious that much of the work was defective. The architect had issued ten Interim Certificates before Mr Sutcliffe entirely lost confidence, dismissed the architect and threw the contractor off the site. He then had the work completed by another contractor and other consultants which cost around £7,000, in addition to which he was obliged, as a result of the original contractor having obtained judgement against him, to pay all ten certificates in full. As this contractor then went bankrupt he then brought a claim against the architects. The architects contended, among other things, that their duty of supervision did not extend to informing the quantity surveyor of defective work that should be excluded from the valuation. HH Judge Stabb QC found for Mr Sutcliffe, stating 'I do not expect that the words "work properly executed" can include work not then properly executed but which it is expected, however confidently, the contractor will remedy in due course' (at page 166).

Unfixed materials and goods

7.8   Certificates should include for materials which have been delivered to the site but not yet incorporated in the Works. Although obliged under the contract to include such items, the contract administrator should be aware that this could result in some considerable risk to the employer. Once materials have been built in, under common law they would normally become the property of the owner of the land, irrespective of whether or not they have been paid for by the contractor. This would be the case even if there were a retention of title clause in the contract with the sub-contractor or supplier. A retention of title clause is one which stipulates that the goods sold do not become the property of the purchaser until they have been paid for, even if they are in the possession of the purchaser.

7.9   The employer could be at risk, however, where materials have not yet been built in, even where the materials have been certified and paid for. The contractor might not actually own the materials paid for because of a retention of title clause in the sale of materials contract. Under the Sale of Goods Act 1979, sections 16–19 property in goods normally passes when the purchaser has possession of them, but a retention of title clause will be effective between a supplier and a contractor even where the contractor has been paid for the goods, provided they have not yet been built in. The employer may have some protection through section 25 of the Act, which in some circumstances allows the employer to treat the contractor as having authority to transfer the title in the goods (see *Archivent v Strathclyde Regional Council* in para 7.10 below).

7.10   Another risk relating to rightful ownership is where the contractor fails to pay a sub-contractor who has purchased materials, and the sub-contractor claims ownership of the unfixed materials. Here the risk may be higher, as a work and materials contract is not governed by the Sale of Goods Act (*Dawber Williams Roofing Ltd* v *Humberside County Council*). Therefore there can be no assumption that property would pass on possession.

Archivent Sales & Developments Ltd v Strathclyde Regional Council (1984) 27 BLR 98
(Court of Session, Outer House)

Archivent agreed to sell a number of ventilators to a contractor who was building a primary school for Strathclyde Regional Council. The contract of sale included the term 'Until payment of the price in full is received by the company, the property in the goods supplied by the company shall not pass to the customer.' The ventilators were delivered and included in a certificate issued under the main contract (JCT63), which was paid. The contractor went into receivership before paying Archivent, who claimed against the Council for the return of the ventilators or a sum representing their value. The Council claimed that section 25 of the Sale of Goods Act operated to give them an unimpeachable title. The judge found for the Council. Even though the clause in the sub-contract successfully retained the title for the sub-contractor, the employer was entitled to the benefit of section 25 of the Sale of Goods Act. The contractor was in possession of the ventilators and had ostensible authority to pass the title on to the employer, who had purchased them in good faith.

Dawber Williams Roofing Ltd v Humberside County Council (1979) 14 BLR 70

The plaintiffs entered into a sub-contract with Taylor and Coulbeck Ltd (T&C) to supply and fix roofing slates. The main contractor's contract with the defendant was on JCT63. By clause 1 of their sub-contract (which was on DOM/1) the plaintiffs were deemed to have notice of all the provisions of the main contract, but it contained no other provisions as to when property was to pass. The plaintiffs delivered 16 tons of roofing slates to the site, which were included in an Interim Certificate, which was paid by the defendant. T&C then went into liquidation without paying the sub-contractor, who brought a claim for the amount or alternatively the return of the slates. The judge allowed the claim, holding that clause 14 of JCT63 could only transfer property where the main contractor had a good title. (The difference between this and the *Archivent* case above is that in this case the sub-contract was a contract for work and materials, to which the Sale of Goods Act did not apply.) Provisions within clause 19·4 of JCT98 now deal with the problem illustrated by this case.

7.11   Unlike IC05 or SBC05, MW05 contains no provisions to protect the employer from these risks. Nevertheless, under MW05 the contract administrator is obliged to include the unfixed materials when certifying progress payments. Clause 4·3·2, however, states that the obligation only extends to materials that are 'properly' delivered, and are adequately stored and protected. Contract administrators should pay careful attention to the exact wording of this qualification.

Retention

7.12   Progress payments are subject to retention (cl 4·3·1), of which half is released after practical completion. The retention percentage is to be five per cent unless another amount is inserted in the Contract Particulars. It would be open to the contract administrator to insert a higher figure, provided that this has been made clear to both parties at the time of tender. This figure might reflect the size and nature of the job, or the economic climate of the time. Five per cent on certain small projects is likely to be so small as to be almost worthless, should the contractor become bankrupt or unexpectedly withdraw from site. If objections are raised at tender stage, it may be worth enquiring what the resulting difference is in the tender figure owing to the higher rate of retention.

7.13   The employer is not stated to be trustee for the beneficiaries of the retention, therefore there is no obligation for the employer to place the retained sum in a separate account. It is sometimes asserted that the contractor has a 'moral' right to this money, but it is difficult to see why this should be the case. It is simply a commercial arrangement to protect the employer, to which the contractor agrees in advance with full knowledge of the consequences. The contract administrator should resist any suggestion that the money be treated in any way other than that set out in the contract itself.

Payment procedure

7.14   Once a progress payment is certified, the final date for payment is 14 days from the date of issue of the certificate (cl 4·3). In practice this timing is rather tight, and it would be sensible to warn the employer in advance of approximately what payment may be required. It is also helpful to include with the certificate a budget update, showing projected total Contract Sum based on any information known at that time regarding variations and provisional sums. This helps the employer to make arrangements for payment in good time.

7.15   Clauses 4·6·1 to 4·6·3 set out requirements for giving notice with regard to progress payment certificates. These clauses are required by the Housing Grants, Construction and Regeneration Act 1996 (ss.110 and 111), and are repeated with respect to the final certificate. The employer must give the contractor notice of how much it intends to pay no later than five days after the certificate is issued (cl 4·6·1). The clause follows the wording of the Act in that the notice is required whether or not the employer intends to make any deduction (*see* Figure 11). The guidance notes issued when this provision first appeared as Amendment 11 to MW80 suggested, however, that the employer would not have to give written notice if no deduction was intended.

7.16   If the employer does intend to withhold any amount, then it may give written notice of this no later than five days before the final date for payment, clearly stating the grounds for making the deduction (cl 4·6·2). The contract then states 'the Employer shall no later than the final date for payment pay the Contractor the amount specified in the notice given under clause 4·6·1 or, in the absence of a notice under clause 4·6·1, the amount stated as due in the certificate' (cl 4·6·3). It is suggested that if it is known in advance that a deduction is intended then the first notice must make this clear. The second notice may then be superfluous, always provided that the first notice included all the necessary information required under clause 4·6·2. If not all information is given, or new circumstances develop following the first notice, then the second notice will be required. In any event many employers might prefer to adopt the cautious and protective line of issuing both notices whenever a deduction is intended.

Deductions

7.17   The contract expressly gives the employer the right to make certain deductions from the certified sums due to the contractor. Notice of the deduction should have been given as described above. Deductions authorised by the contract arise in respect of:

- payment or allowance of liquidated damages (cl 2·8·1);

- non-compliance with contract administrator's instructions (cl 3·4).

Employer's obligation to pay

7.18   It is now generally agreed that in cases where the employer has a right to make a deduction, this can only be exercised through the use of the 'withholding notice' procedure as discussed above. The employer would therefore be unable to withhold amounts to cover any defective work included in a certificate, unless the deduction is covered by a notice (*Rupert Morgan Building Services (CCC) Ltd* v *David Jervis and Hamlet Jervis*). The rights of the employer when defects appear after the expiry of the time limits for notices, but before the final date for payment, are unclear, but it is arguable that in such situations the employer would retain a right to abatement of the amount due.

Gilbert-Ash (Northern) Ltd v Modern Engineering (Bristol) Ltd (1974) 1 BLR 73 (HL)

Bradford City Council employed Gilbert-Ash as main contractor under JCT63. Modern Engineering was the sub-contractor for steelwork on a non-standard sub-contract drafted by Gilbert-Ash. The main contract stated that the main contractor should pay to the sub-contractor any amounts stated by the contract administrator as due to the sub-contractor under an Interim Certificate. Clause 14 of the sub-contract stated: 'if the Sub-contractor fails to comply with any of the conditions of this Sub-contract the Contractor reserves the right to suspend or withhold payment of any monies due or becoming due to the Sub-contractor'.

The contract administrator issued three Interim Certificates certifying that the total amount due in respect of the sub-contractor's work was £14,532 18s 10p, but out of that sum the contractor paid the sub-contractor only £10,000. Modern Engineering issued a writ claiming the balance. The main contractor issued a defence which asserted that it had claims against the sub-contractor for losses caused by delay and defective work. The question in issue was whether the main contractor had bound itself to pay sums in Interim Certificates without any right to set-off claims in respect of breaches of contract by the sub-contractor. The judge at first instance decided in favour of the contractor, and the sub-contractor appealed. The Court of Appeal reversed the decision, and the dispute was taken to the House of Lords. The House stated that the Common law right of a defendant to set up a breach of warranty in diminution or extinction of an instalment of a sum which had become due could only be excluded by clear, unequivocal words. There was no provision in the main contract that excluded this right.

C. M. Pillings & Co Ltd v Kent Investments Ltd (1985) 30 BLR 80 (CA)

The defendants employed the plaintiffs for work to a house on the JCT Fixed Fee Form of Prime Cost Contract. Following practical completion the contract administrator issued a certificate for over £100,000, which was not paid, and the contractor commenced legal proceedings, applying for summary judgement under Order 14. The defendant applied for a stay so that the matter could go to arbitration. The trial judge stayed the action and the contractor appealed. The appeal was dismissed. The court found that the effect of the terms of the contract was not that the certificate gave the contractor the right to immediate summary judgement for the amount. As the commentators stated: 'The issue of a certificate creates a debt and the burden is then upon the debtor to show that the amount apparently due is not owing'. If an arguable case can be shown, the matter can be decided at arbitration and payment of the certificate is not a condition precedent to this taking place.

Rupert Morgan Building Services (CCC) Ltd v David Jervis and Hamlet Jervis [2003] EWCA Cir 1583 (CA)

A couple engaged a builder to have work done on their cottage, by means of a contract on the standard form published by the Architecture and Surveying Institute ('ASI'). The 7th Interim Certificate was for a sum of around £44,000 plus VAT. The clients accepted that part of that amount was payable but disputed the balance amounting to some £27,000. The builders sought judgement for the balance. The clients did not give 'a notice of intention to withhold payment' before 'the prescribed period before the final date for payment'. The builders argued that it followed, by virtue of s.111(1) that the clients 'may not withhold payment'. The clients maintained that it was open to them by way of defence to prove that the items of work which go to make up the unpaid balance were not done at all, or were duplications of items already paid or were charged as extras when they were within the original contract, or represent 'snagging' for Works already done and paid for. The Court of Appeal determined that in the absence of an effective withholding notice the employer has no right to set off against a contract administrator's certificate.

Contractor's position if the certificate is not paid

7.19   MW05 includes several provisions which protect the contractor if the employer fails to pay the contractor amounts due. Clause 4·4 and the Contract Particulars make provision for simple interest on late payments of certificates. This is set at five per cent over the Base Rate of the Bank of England, and the interest accrues from the final date for payment until the amount is paid. Similar provisions are included for the final certificate. If the employer makes a valid deduction following a proper notice it is suggested that interest would not be due on this amount. The clause does not refer to the amount stated on the certificate but to 'the amount due to the Contractor' which would take into account valid deductions.

7.20   The contractor is also given a 'right of suspension' under clause 4·7. This right is required by the Housing Grants, Construction and Regeneration Act 1996. If the employer fails to pay the contractor by the final date for payment the contractor has a right to suspend performance of all its obligations under the contract, which would include not only the carrying out of the work but, for example, could also extend to any insurance obligations. This right is stated to be 'subject to any notice issued pursuant to clause 4·6·2', which suggests that the contractor may not suspend work if a notice to withhold payment has been given by the employer. The contractor must have given the employer written notice of its intention to suspend work and stated the grounds for the suspension, and the default must have continued for a further seven days.

7.21   The contractor must resume work when the payment is made. Under these circumstances the suspension would not give the employer the right to determine the contractor's employment. Any delay caused by the suspension could be a matter beyond the control of the contractor in relation to an extension of time. The contractor also has the right to determine the contract if the employer does not pay amounts properly due (cl 6·8·1·1). The contractor must give notice of this intention, which specifies the default as required by the contract.

Certificate not issued or undervalued

7.22   The issue of a certificate is a condition precedent of the right of the contractor to be paid (*Lubenham* v *South Pembrokeshire District Council*). This case states that the contractor is only entitled to the sum stated in the certificate, even if the certificate contains an error, for example because it includes a wrongful deduction. The contractor's remedy is to request that the error is corrected in the next certificate, or to bring proceedings to have the certificate adjusted. There are exceptions to this rule where, for example, the employer has interfered with the issue of the certificate, in which case the contractor may be entitled to summary judgement for the correct amount.

Lubenham Fidelities and Investments Co Ltd v South Pembrokeshire District Council (1986) 33 BLR 39 (CA)

Lubenham Fidelities was a bondsman who elected to complete two building contracts, both based on JCT63. The architects, Wigley Fox Partnership, issued several Interim Certificates which stated the total value of work carried out, but also made deductions for liquidated damages and defective work from the face of the certificate. Lubenham protested that the certificates had not been correctly calculated, withdrew its contractors from the site and issued notices to determine the contract. Shortly after, the Council gave notice of determination of the contract.

Lubenham brought a claim against the Council claiming that its notices were valid and effective, and against Wigley Fox on the basis that their negligence had caused it losses. It was held that the Council was not obliged to pay more than the amount on the certificate, and that whatever the cause of the undervaluation the correct procedure was not to withdraw labour, but to request that the error was corrected in the next certificate, or to pursue the matter in arbitration. Lubenham's claim against Wigley Fox failed because it had been the suspension of the Works rather than the certificates that had caused the losses, and because the architects had not acted with the intention of interfering with the performance of the contract.

Penultimate certificate

7.23   The contract administrator must issue a certificate within 14 days of the date of practical completion certified under clause 2·9 (cl 4·5). This should be for 97.5 per cent (unless a different percentage was inserted in Contract Particulars clause 4·3) of the total amount due to the contractor under the contract, in so far as it can be ascertained at that stage. The effect would therefore normally be to release to the contractor half of the retention that has been deducted. The precise final amount due to the contractor might not be known at this stage, but a reasonably accurate calculation should be made based on all available information. The employer is obliged to pay within 14 days of the date of issue, and the provisions regarding notices discussed above apply also to this certificate. The certificate is of particular importance in that it has been held to be a condition precedent to the issue of a valid final certificate (see *Crestar* v *John and Joy Carr* at 7.28 below).

Final Certificate

7.24   To summarise, by final certificate stage the following certificates should have been issued:

- Progress Payment certificates at four weekly intervals (cl 4·3);

- Practical Completion Certificate (cl 2·9);

- penultimate certificate following practical completion, including release of half of the retention (cl 4·5);

- Certificate of Making Good (cl 2·11).

Figure 11 Payment procedure

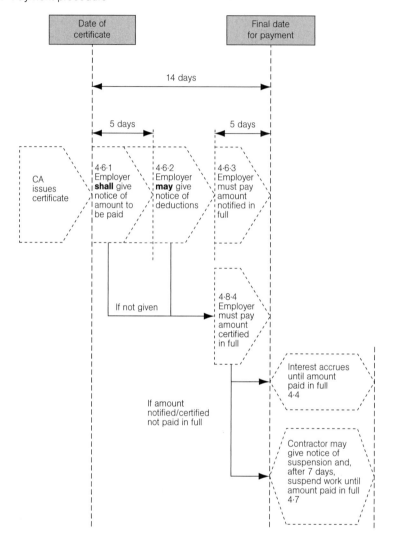

The date for issuing the final certificate will be determined by whether the contract administrator has certified that the contractor has discharged obligations concerning defects at the end of the Rectification Period, and by whether the contractor has supplied sufficient documentation for the preparation of the final account (see Figure 11). The contractor must send the information 'reasonably required' within three months of the date of practical completion certified by the contract administrator. Where the contract administrator finds that the information is inadequate, then any outstanding information should be asked for immediately. The contract administrator is obliged to issue the Final Certificate within 28 days of receipt of the documentation 'reasonably required', and although it might be considered good practice to allow the contractor time to consider the draft final account, there is no such requirement and the time-scale could be tight in some instances.

7.25 The Final Certificate must state the basis of calculation, and the amount remaining due to the contractor. The certificate could, in unusual circumstances, be for a negative amount – in other words it could certify that payment is due from the contractor to the employer. The certificate is subject to the same rights to make deductions as are discussed in para 7.17 above. The time for final payment is 14 days from the date of issue of the certificate, which means that the time allowed for issuing the notices required under the contract is extremely tight.

Conclusive effect of Final Certificate

7.26 The Final Certificate is not stated to be conclusive evidence that any obligations under the contract have been discharged. It is important to point this out, as the conclusive effect of the Final Certificate has been the subject of much heated debate following the decisions in *Colbart Ltd* v *H. Kumar* and *Crown Estate Commissioners* v *John Mowlem*.

7.27 Neither of these cases concerned the Minor Works Agreement, where the wording of the relevant clauses is quite different, and the approach taken in *Crown Estate Commissioners* v *John Mowlem* has not been applied to that form. Earlier cases which did consider the Minor Works Agreement such as *Crestar* v *John and Joy Carr* reached a quite different conclusion as to the effect of the final certificate. Moreover, the decision of the House of Lords in *Beaufort Developments* v *Gilbert-Ash*, which overruled the decision of *Northern Regional Health Authority* v *Derek Crouch Construction Co*, suggests a reversal in the trend to treat certificates under construction contracts as incapable of challenge except in limited circumstances. Although *Beaufort Developments* did not overrule or consider the decision in *Crown Estate Commissioners* it would seem very unlikely that a court would now take the approach adopted in that case.

7.28 It is perhaps worth pointing out that although neither the Final Certificate nor any other certificate is stated to be conclusive, there may remain a very limited area where it would be difficult to raise a challenge. This could occur where the contract administrator has not specified any objective standards against which a decision could be reviewed, and no such standards could be implied. For example, if the contract administrator has merely indicated that the colour of the paint should be 'apple green' and 'to the satisfaction of the architect', if the contract administrator includes for painting work in a certificate, it may be very difficult for the employer to later claim that the colour of the paint is unsatisfactory. Although in theory the certificate could be challenged, there would be no means by which it could be proved the contractor was in breach. The message is clear – always specify objective and measurable standards.

Crestar Ltd v Michael John Carr and Joy Carr (1987) 37 BLR 113 (CA)

John and Joy Carr employed Crestar on the Minor Works Form (pre-1980 version) to carry out work on their house. The contract price was £70,634. Crestar claimed they had done additional work to the value of around £46,000. The work was finished about June 1985, and on 1 October 1985 the architect issued a Final Certificate in the sum of £39,575, which valued the additional work at £49,690. Prior to the Final Certificate, the owners had paid all amounts certified but they did not pay this amount. On 22 October Crestar issued a writ for the amount certified and the Carrs applied for a stay, on the grounds that the contract contained an arbitration clause.

The Carrs' application was granted by the district registrar and Crestar appealed. The court dismissed the appeal and Crestar then appealed again, claiming that the effect of the Final Certificate was that the employer could not bring a claim in arbitration after 14 days from the date of its issue as it then constituted a debt due, and the certificate became final and conclusive as to the quality of the Works. Fox LJ, dismissing the appeal, pointed out that the Conditions assumed that by the time of the Final Certificate the employer would normally have been presented with a certificate and have paid 95 per cent of the amount due following practical completion. As no penultimate certificate had been issued, the certificate issued in October was not a valid Final Certificate under the terms of the contract.

However, even if it had been valid there was nothing in the contract that made it conclusive of any matters. He stated:

> There is nothing in the arbitration provisions to prevent it (the employer raising a defence). There is nothing in any other Conditions of the contract to prevent it save, it is said, the word 'debt'. I do not think that is sufficient: it places undue weight upon the term . . . I am not prepared to infer that the parties intended to prevent the owners referring matters to arbitration after the end of the 14-day period. Important defects in work or materials which were not apparent upon reasonable inspection prior to the expiry of the 14-day period may become apparent later . . . (at page 124)

Crown Estate Commissioners v John Mowlem & Co Ltd (1994) 70 BLR 1 (CA)

Crown Estates employed Mowlem to construct a commercial development on the site of the former Kensington Palace Barracks. A Final Certificate was issued on 2 December 1992, and on 6 April 1993 Crown Estates gave notice of arbitration. They then issued a summons under section 27 of the Arbitration Act for an order extending the time within which to commence arbitration, in order to validate their notice. In addition to the summons the judge at first instance was also asked to consider the question as to what, if anything, the final certificate was conclusive evidence of, as this would affect what could be raised in the arbitration. The judge issued the order extending time and held that the Final Certificate was only conclusive as to matters that were expressly stated to be for the satisfaction of the architect. Mowlem appealed and the appeal was allowed. The Court of Appeal stated that clauses 30·9·1·1 and 30·9·3 did not limit the time within which arbitration proceedings could be brought, therefore the court had no powers under the Arbitration Act that could defeat the effect of the certificate. It also held that as all standards and quality of work and materials were inherently matters for the opinion of the architect, the Final Certificate was conclusive evidence of all such matters.

---

8 Indemnity and insurance

8.1   Even small-scale operations carry risks, particularly those relating to work on existing buildings. It is often the case with such work, where the programme may be tight and arrangements anything but straightforward, that matters of insurance are not dealt with as promptly or as thoroughly as they might be. It is important that liability for losses resulting from personal injury, damage to property, or to the Works, is agreed beforehand and clearly allocated to one party or the other, and that the liability is backed up by appropriate insurance cover. In seeking to protect the employer's interests the architect should have a knowledge of the relevant contract clauses sufficient to be able to explain their purpose and what they mean.

8.2   Most building contracts provide for the contractor to indemnify the employer in respect of certain losses, for example for injury to persons, or damage to neighbouring property which has been caused by the contractor's negligence, and in MW05 this is done under clauses 5·1 and 5·2. This indemnity protects the employer in that if an injured party brings an action against the employer, rather than against the contractor, the latter has agreed to carry the consequences of the claim. If a third party sues the employer, then the employer can join the contractor as co-defendant or bring separate proceedings. Indemnities given to the employer by the contractor will obviously be quite worthless unless there are adequate resources to meet claims. The contract therefore requires insurance cover to back up the indemnities.

8.3   In addition to the requirement for insurance against claims arising in respect of persons and property, the contract also contains alternative provisions for insurance of the Works under clauses 5·4A, 5·4B, and 5·4C. 5·4A is for use with new buildings, and is taken out by the contractor, 5·4B is for use with existing buildings where the policy will also cover the new works, and is taken out by the employer, and 5·4C is used where the employer insures the existing building, and the contractor insures the works under 5·4A. It should be noted that MW05 makes no provision for 'Terrorism Cover' or for compliance with the Joint Fire Code.

8.4   Neither does MW05 include provisions for insurance against damage caused to property which is not the result of the negligence of the contractor. For example, subsidence or vibration resulting from the carrying out of the Works might cause such damage, even though the contractor has taken reasonable care. This is a risk which may be quite high with certain projects on tight urban sites, or in close proximity to old buildings, and in such cases it might be advisable to take out a special policy for the benefit of the employer. If this type of insurance is desired then it may be possible to import an adapted wording of IC05 clause 6·5, requiring the contractor to take out such insurance, but specialist advice should be sought. This insurance is usually expensive, and subject to a great many exceptions. If it is required, then the policy needs to be effective at the start of the site operations when demolition, excavation, etc are carried out.

8.5   The contractor must be able to provide evidence upon reasonable request that the insurances referred to under clauses 5·1, 5·2, 5·3 and 5·4A have been taken out. Where the contractor elects to cover 'the Works' under an existing 'All Risks' policy then this should be appropriately endorsed and recognise the employer as a joint insured. There is no provision for what will occur if the contractor defaults; in such cases the employer would have taken out the insurance and could bring a claim against the contractor.

8.6   The employer is obliged to produce to the contractor, upon reasonable request, evidence that insurance referred to in clause 5·4B·1 is in force, and appropriately endorsed with the name of the contractor as the joint insured. This clause deals with two distinct matters – damage to the employer's existing building and its contents, and damage to the Works including unfixed materials or goods intended for the contract. There must be joint names insurance in force, and this insurance must be arranged by the employer.

Injury to persons

8.7   Clause 5·1 covers injury to persons which arise from the carrying out of the Works. The contractor is liable and indemnifies the employer, but the liability and duty to indemnify are subject to the exception that the contractor is not liable where injury or death is caused by an act of the employer, or a person for whom the employer is responsible (cl 5·1).

8.8   The contractor's liability in respect of personal injury or death of employees is met by an employer's liability policy. This has been compulsory since the Employer's Liability (Compulsory Insurance) Act 1969. The contractor's liability in respect of third parties (death or personal injury and loss or damage to property including consequential loss) is met by its public liability policy. Insurers typically advocate insuring for a minimum of £2 million for any one occurrence, and may recommend cover of £5 million or more in exceptional cases. Liability at Common law for claims by third parties is, however, unlimited. There is no opportunity to enter a minimum requirement in the contract. Clause 5·3·1 refers to 'all relevant legislation', which would also cover, for example, insurance requirements under the Road Traffic Act 1988.

Damage to property

8.9   Clause 5·2 covers damage to property real or personal, which arises from the carrying out of the Works. The Works, including unfixed goods and materials, are expressly excluded from the definition of property in this context. The contractor is required to match the indemnity given with appropriate insurance to a level inserted in the clause.

8.10   The minimum figure for which the contractor is required to take out insurance cover should be entered in the Contract Particulars (clause 5·3·2), and is unlikely to be less than £2 million. This would be a contractual minimum, and in no way limits the contractor's liability to the sum entered.

8.11   The contractor is only liable to the extent that the damage is caused by negligence or breach of statutory duty or other default of 'the Contractor, his servants or agents, or of any person employed or engaged by the Contractor upon or in connection with the Works or any part thereof, his servants or agents' (cl 5·2). The contractor is therefore liable only for losses caused by its own negligence. Clause 5·2 also excludes liability for loss or damage 'where clause 5·4B applies, to any property required to be insured thereunder caused by a Specified Peril'. This means that, where clause 5·4B is applicable, the contractor is not liable for losses insured under that clause and caused by the listed perils, even where the damage is caused by the contractor's own negligence. The phrase quoted was inserted to clarify matters following a series of cases which reached the opposite conclusion (*National Trust* v *Haden Young, Barking & Dagenham* v *Stamford Asphalt Co*). Domestic sub-contractors, however, may be liable for losses caused by their negligence (*BT* v *James Thompson & Sons*). It should be noted, also, that the contractor might remain liable for some consequential losses (*Kruger Tissue* v *Frank Galliers*).

The National Trust for Places of Historic Interest and Natural Beauty v Haden Young Ltd (1994) 72 BLR 1 (CA)

The National Trust employed a contractor to carry out repair works to Uppark House, South Harting, West Sussex. The main contract was on terms substantially similar to MW80. Haden Young were sub-contractors for the renewal of lead work on the roof. During the course of the Works a fire broke out, causing extensive damage, which Hayden Young admitted was caused by the negligence of their workforce, and the National Trust brought a clam for damages. Otton J found the sub-contractors liable at first instance, and that the employer's liability to insure under clause 5·4B only extended to matters not caused by negligence. Clauses 5·2 and 5·4B formed a coherent and mutually supportive structure. Haden Young appealed, but the appeal was dismissed. Although the Court of Appeal agreed that the sub-contractor was liable, it disagreed with the reasoning of the lower court, stating that there was no reason why there should not be an overlap, in other words why the employer should not be required to insure for matters for which the contractor was liable under clause 6·2. However, the damages recoverable from the contractor under clause 6. would be reduced by the amount recoverable by the employer under the clause 6·3B insurance.

London Borough of Barking & Dagenham v Stamford Asphalt Co Ltd (1997) 82 BLR 25 (CA)

Barking & Dagenham employed a contractor to carry out repair works to a school. The main contract was on MW80, 1988 revision. Stamford were sub-contractors for the renewal of lead work on the roof. During the course of the Works a fire broke out, causing extensive damage, which Stamford admitted was caused by the negligence of their workforce, and the Borough brought a claim for damages. The Court of Appeal found the contractor liable for the damage caused, preferring the reasoning of Otton J in *National Trust* v *Haden Young* to that of the Court of Appeal In that case. It should be noted that the wording of clause 6·2 (now cl 5·2) has now been adjusted to make it clear that the contractor is not liable for damage to property insured under clause 6·3B (now cl 5·4B).

British Telecommunications plc v James Thompson & Sons (Engineers) Ltd (1999) 1 BLR 35 (HL)

James Thompson were sub-contractors on a refurbishment project for British Telecom. A fire broke out in the roof area while the sub-contractors were carrying out their work. The court found that the relevant clauses had the same effect as the equivalent clauses considered in *SSHA* v *Wimpey*.

However, they decided that domestic sub-contractors remained under a duty of care to prevent such losses, and were therefore liable to BT under the tort of negligence. They considered that the wording of clause 22·3, which required the joint names policies to waive the rights of subrogation against nominated but not domestic sub-contractors, should be taken into account in considering whether a duty of care existed. The fact that BT were indemnified by the clause 22C insurers, even if the fire was caused by the sub-contractors, was not sufficient to prevent the imposition of the duty.

Kruger Tissue (Industrial) Ltd v Frank Galliers Ltd (1998) 57 ConLR 1

Damage was caused to existing buildings and Works by flare, assumed for the purposes of the case to be the result of the negligence of the contractor or sub-contractor. The employers brought a claim for loss of profits, increased cost of working and consultants' fees, all of which are consequential losses. Judge John Hicks decided that the employer's duty to insure for 'the full cost of reinstatement, repair or replacement of the existing structure and the Works under clause 22C (and therefore contractor's exemption from liability under clause 20·2·3), did not include such consequential losses'. A claim could therefore be brought against the contractor for these.

Insurance of the Works

8.12   There are three alternative clauses for insuring the Works (cl 5·4A, 5·4B and 5·4C) and the reference to the clause or clauses which are not applicable should be deleted in the Contract Particulars. A footnote to the appropriate entry explains that 5·4A or 5·4B may be selected on its own, but that 5·4C would always be used in conjunction with 5·4A.

8.13   The policies under 5·4A or 5·4B are to be in joint names ('Joint Names' is defined under clause 1·1), and the insurer waives any rights to recover any of the monies from either of the named parties or from any person recognised as insured under the policy. The cover must run until practical completion of the Works, or termination if this should occur earlier (cl 5·4A·1 and 5·4B·1).

8.14   Clause 5·4A is intended for insuring new building work. It requires the contractor to take out 'All Risks' Insurance against loss or damage to the Works and unfixed goods and materials (the term 'All Risks' is defined under clause 1·1). The insurance should be for the full reinstatement value of the Works (which is likely to be more than the original tender figure). It must include for professional fees likely to arise should damage occur, at the percentage entered in the clause.

8.15   The contractor is responsible for keeping the Works fully covered, and in the event of under-insurance will be liable for any shortfall in recovery from the insurers. Care needs to be taken over identifying the extent of 'the Works' exactly.

8.16   Clause 5·4B is applicable where work is being carried out to existing buildings. The existing structure, the contents owned by the employer 'or for which he is responsible', and the Works must be insured under an 'All Risks' policy. Sometimes the employer has difficulty in obtaining this insurance: either the building may be historic or particularly sensitive and therefore extremely difficult to insure or, in the case of small domestic projects, the insurers may refuse to extend cover when they are informed about impending work. The employer should be warned well in advance if this insurance will be required.

8.17　　In the event that the employer cannot obtain insurance under 5·4B, the contractor may need to insure the Works under 5·4A, as is indicated in footnote 16 to the Contract Particulars and discussed in the Guidance Note to the form. The employer will maintain insurance for the existing building under 5·4C, but the arrangement must be discussed with both insurance companies in order to avoid duplication of cover. Should difficulties arise the employer should always ask to deal with the head office of the insurance company, and may need to seek expert advice.

Action following damage to the Works

8.18　　Although the contract does not require it, it would be implied that the contractor should inform the contract administrator as soon as any damage occurs. The insurers should be immediately informed. Under clause 5·4A·2·1, after any inspection required has been made by the insurers, the contractor is then obliged to make good the damage and continue with the Works.

8.19　　All monies due under the insurance policy are normally paid direct to the employer. The insurance money paid to the employer, minus the part of it to cover professional fees, should be included in future certificates as the work is carried out. If the amount paid by the insurers is less than it costs the contractor to rebuild the Works, the contractor is not entitled to any additional payment. The risk of any under-insurance therefore lies with the contractor.

8.20　　Under clause 5·4B·2 the contract administrator must issue instructions regarding the rebuilding work, which is treated as if it were a variation under clause 3·6·1. The contract must authorise that all monies are paid direct to the employer (cl 5·4B·1). The contractor is less at risk as the employer will have to bear any shortfall in the monies paid out. In addition, as the work is treated as a variation, the contractor may be entitled to loss and/or expense.

8.21　　Under clause 2·7 the contractor might be entitled to an extension of time for delay caused by the events, except it is suggested that this would not extend to cases where the damage was caused by the contractor's negligence.

8.22　　Though the contract does not require it, it is common practice to keep the reinstatement work distinct by issuing 'reinstatement certificates' which cover only that work, at the same intervals as the Progress Payment certificates. Certificates that have already been issued and the amounts paid or due under them are of course not affected by the occurrence of the damage. Any work that was completed after the most recent Progress Payment certificate, but was then subsequently damaged, should also be included in the next certificate.

8.23   MW05 contains provisions enabling either party to determine the employment of the contractor in the event that work is suspended for a period of one month or more as a result of loss or damage to the Works caused by one of the Specified Perils (cl 6·10·1·3). It is suggested that: this right would normally only be exercised where the damage was so extensive as to make it impracticable or impossible to continue with the Works; if the damage is limited it will normally be in both parties' interests to continue under the existing contract. It should be noted that the contractor is not entitled to terminate the contract if the Specified Peril was caused by its own negligence (cl 6·10·2).

The contract administrator's role in insurance

8.24   The insurance provisions in MW05 might appear to indicate no role for the contract administrator. But he or she will be required to make entries in clauses 5·2 and 5·4 if relevant, and it may be implied that the contract administrator has a duty to explain the provisions in the contract to the employer. The contract administrator will keep a watch on the actions of the parties, although insurance matters may appear to be conducted almost directly between them. He or she is primarily a channel of communication, and although responsibility for policies rests primarily with the contractor or the employer and their insurance advisers, the contract administrator should check the wording of policies and any endorsements to see that there are no obvious inconsistencies with the Contract Documents.

8.25   The contract administrator should therefore have a reasonable knowledge of the indemnity and insurance provisions of MW05 although he or she would not be expected to be an expert. It may be that difficulties arise in obtaining cover for certain types of building, or the cost of insurance becomes uneconomic and the employer wishes to adopt a policy of no insurance. It could be that insurers are reluctant to give joint names cover on existing domestic structures, or may well seek to impose special conditions. In particular the relationship between the employer's existing insurance arrangements and those required under the contract can be very tricky, and on matters such as these the employer must be advised to consult its own insurance experts.

8.26   If accidents do occur on site and injury or damage results, the contract administrator must be alert to the fact that such matters must be reported quickly to the insurers. If damage to the Works requires inspection by the insurers, then the contract administrator might be expected to be in attendance or to supply information. If loss or damage results which is the direct responsibility of the employer under clause 5·4B·2, then the contract administrator is required to issue instructions for the reinstatement, and to value the work as may be necessary.

9 Termination

9.1 At the outset of a contract the parties almost invariably approach it in good faith and with the best of intentions but, in spite of this, breaches of contract sometimes occur. Some of these are minor technicalities, and some can be dealt with by the machinery of the contract. Others are more serious and can only be dealt with by more drastic measures.

Repudiation or termination

9.2 Most building contracts include provisions to deal with foreseeable situations which might otherwise be breaches. For example, where the contractor is unable to complete by the completion date due to circumstances entirely beyond its control, then an extension of time can be awarded. Where the employer wishes to vary the work after the contract has been let, then this is possible under clause 3·6. However, if such machinery is not included in a contract, or is not operated as it should be, then the injured party may be able to claim damages for breach of contract. Such claims would have to go to adjudication, arbitration or litigation.

9.3 It sometimes happens that the behaviour of one party makes it difficult or impossible for the other to carry out the obligations of the contract. The injured party might then allege prevention of performance and sue either for damages or a *quantum meruit*.

9.4 Or, where it is impossible to expect any further performance, the injured party might allege that the contract has been repudiated. Repudiation is when one party makes it clear that it no longer intends to be bound by the provisions of the contract. This might be expressly stated, or implied by the party's behaviour.

9.5 Most JCT contracts include termination clauses, which provide for the effective termination of the employment of the contractor in circumstances which may amount to, or which may fall short of, repudiation. (If there is repudiation, invoking a termination clause is unnecessary, because the injured party can accept the repudiation and bring the contract to an end.) It should be noted that the termination is of the contractor's employment, and is not termination of the contract. In effect termination removes the need for further performance, but leaves the parties still bound by other provisions. Termination provisions, such as those set out in MW05 section 6, are useful in setting out the exact circumstances, procedures and consequences of the termination of employment. However, these procedures must be followed with great caution because if they are not administered strictly in accordance with the terms of the contract, this in itself could amount to a repudiation. This, in turn, might give the other party the right to treat the contract as at an end and claim damages.

9.6 Under MW05 the employer has the right to terminate the contractor's employment in the event of specified defaults by the contractor such as suspending the carrying out of the

Works (cl 6·4), or in the event of the insolvency of the contractor (cl 6·5), or in the event that the contractor has committed an offence under the Prevention of Corruption Acts (cl 6·6). Termination can be initiated by the contractor in the event of specified defaults by the employer such as failure to pay the amount due on a certificate, or causing the work to be suspended for a period of more than one month (cl 6·8). Termination might also follow the insolvency of the employer. Termination may be initiated by either party in the event of neutral causes which might cause the work to be suspended for a period of one month or more (cl 6·10).

Termination by the employer

9.7   The contract provides for termination of the employment of the contractor under stated circumstances. MW05 expressly states that the right to determine the contractor's employment is 'without prejudice to any other rights and remedies' (cl 6·3·1). This termination can be initiated by the employer in the event of specified defaults by the contractor occurring prior to practical completion (cl 6·4·2), which comprise suspending of the carrying out of the Works or also, in the case of MWD05, the design of the CDP (cl 6·4·1·1), failing to proceed regularly or diligently with either of these (cl 6·4·1·2), and breach of the CDM Regulations (cl 6·4·1·3). The employer may also terminate in the event of insolvency or corruption of the contractor (cl 6·5 and 6·6). Upon termination the contractor must immediately leave the site; the employer need not make any further payment until the Works are complete (cl 6·7·2), and may recover any losses resulting from the termination from the contractor (cl 6·7·3·1).

9.8   The procedures as set out in the contract must be followed exactly, especially those concerning the issue of notices under clause 6·4. If default occurs the contract administrator should issue a warning notice, specifying the default and requiring it to be ended. If the default is not ended within seven days from receipt of the notice then the employer may terminate the employment of the contractor by the issue of a further notice within ten days from the expiry of that seven-day period, which takes effect from the date of receipt (cl 6·4·2). Unlike SBC05 and IC05 there is no provision for 'repeat' defaults, if this occurs it is likely that a further warning notice will be needed. In the case of insolvency or corruption only one notice is required, to be issued by the employer (cl 6·5·1 and 6·6). It should be noted that to be valid all notices must be in writing and given by actual delivery, or by special or recorded delivery (cl 6·2). This rules out e-mail or fax transmissions. Notices sent by post are deemed to have been received 48 hours after posting (excluding weekends and public holidays), unless there is proof to the contrary. As time limits are of vital importance it might be wise to have receipt of delivery confirmed.

9.9   The grounds for termination by the employer under clause 6·4·1 include failing to proceed diligently, wholly or substantially suspending the carrying out of work, and failing to comply with obligations under the CDM Regulations. The grounds must be clearly established and expressed as the contract clearly states that termination must not be exercised unreasonably or vexatiously (cl 6·2·1). For example, for a breach of the CDM Regulations to merit termination, it should be a reasonably serious breach so as to cause a significant risk to health and safety, and/or risk of prosecution by the Health and Safety Executive. It should be noted that the defaults must occur 'without reasonable cause' on the contractor's part, and that, depending on the circumstances, the contractor might find 'reasonable cause' in any of the matters referred to in clause 6·8·1. An exercise of the new right to suspend work given by the Housing Grants, Construction and Regeneration Act 1996 would not be cause for termination, provided that it had been exercised in accordance with the terms of the contract.

9.10 One of the defaults listed in clause 6·4·1·2 is that the contractor 'fails to proceed regularly and diligently'. This is notoriously difficult to establish, and although meticulous records will help, architects are often understandably reluctant to issue the first warning notice. Reported cases show how difficult this can be in practice. In the case of *London Borough of Hounslow v Twickenham Garden Developments*, for example, the architect's notice was heavily attacked by the defendants. In a more recent case, however, the architect was found negligent because he failed to issue a notice (*West Faulkner Associates v London Borough of Newham*). It should be remembered that without the first 'warning notice' issued by the architect the employer cannot issue the termination notice.

London Borough of Hounslow v Twickenham Garden Developments (1970) 7 BLR 81

The London Borough of Hounslow entered into a contract with Twickenham Garden Developments to carry out sub-structure works at Heston and Isleworth in Middlesex. The contract was on JCT63. Work on the contract stopped for approximately eight months due to a strike. After work resumed, the architects issued a notice of default stating that the contractor had failed to proceed regularly and diligently and that unless there was an appreciable improvement the contract would be determined. The employer then proceeded to determine the contractor's employment. The contractor disputed the validity of the notices and the termination, and refused to stop work and leave the site. The Borough applied to the court for an injunction to remove the contractor. The judge emphasised that an injunction was a serious remedy and that before he could grant one there had to be clear and indisputable evidence of the merits of its case. The evidence put before him, which showed a significant drop in the amounts of monthly certificates and numbers of workmen on site, failed to provide this.

West Faulkner Associates v London Borough of Newham (1992) 61 BLR 81

West Faulkner were architects engaged by the Borough for the refurbishment of a housing estate consisting of several blocks of flats. The residents of the estate were evacuated from their flats in stages to make way for the contractors, Moss, whom it had been agreed would carry out the work according to a programme of phased possession and completion, with each block to take nine weeks. Moss fell behind the programme almost immediately. However, they had a large workforce on the site and continually promised to revise their programme and working methods to address the problems of lateness, poor quality work and unsafe working practices that were drawn to their attention on numerous occasions by the architects. In reality Moss remained completely disorganised, and there was no apparent improvement. The architects took the advice of quantity surveyors that the grounds of failing to proceed regularly and diligently would be difficult to prove, and decided not to issue a notice. As a consequence the Borough was unable to issue a notice of termination, had to negotiate a settlement with the contractors and dismissed the architects, who then brought a claim for their fees.

The judge decided that the architects were in breach of contract in failing to give proper consideration to the use of the termination provisions. In his judgement he stated that 'regularly and diligently' should be construed together and in essence they mean simply that the contractors must go about their work in such a way as to achieve their contractual obligations. 'This requires them to plan their work, to lead and manage their workforce, to provide sufficient and proper materials and to employ competent tradesmen, so that the Works are carried out to an acceptable standard and that all time, sequence and other provisions are fulfilled' (Judge Newey at page 139).

Insolvency of the contractor

9.11   Insolvency is the inability to pay debts as they become due for payment. Insolvent individuals may be declared bankrupt. Insolvent companies may be dealt with in a number of ways depending upon the circumstances, for example by voluntary liquidation (in which the company resolves to wind itself up), compulsory liquidation (under which the company is wound up by a court order), administrative receivership (a procedure to assist the rescue of a company under appointed receivers), an administration order (a court order given in response to a petition, again with the aim of rescue rather than liquidation, and managed by an appointed receiver), or voluntary arrangement (in which the company agrees terms with creditors over payment of debts). Procedures for dealing with insolvency are mainly subject to the Insolvency Act 1986 and the Insolvency Rules. Under these the person authorised to oversee statutory insolvency procedures is termed an insolvency practitioner.

9.12   Under MW05 (cl 6·5·1) the employer has the right to terminate the contract in the event that the contractor is 'Insolvent' as defined under clause 6·1. The contractual definition covers a wide range of situations including voluntary arrangements and winding up or bankruptcy orders. There is no requirement for the contractor to notify the employer in writing in the event of liquidation or insolvency, but as it is likely that such a requirement would be implied, the contractor might be expected to do this.

9.13   As termination is not automatic, the employer has, in effect, an option to consider a more constructive approach. If this is found not to be practicable, then the only option will be for the employer to determine, and the only way to achieve completion will be by a new contractor of the employer's choice. In some circumstances, however, it may be sensible to allow an appointed insolvency practitioner time to come up with a rescue package. It is usually in the employer's interest to have the Works completed with as little additional delay and cost as possible, and a breathing space might allow all possibilities to be explored. It may, for example, be possible for the contractor to continue and complete the Works, provided funding can be arranged.

9.14   If the original contractor cannot continue, another contractor may be novated to complete the Works. On a 'true novation', the substitute contractor would take over all the original obligations and benefits (including completion to time and within Contract Sum). More likely is a 'conditional novation' whereby the contract completion date, etc would be subject to re-negotiation, and the substitute contractor would probably want to disclaim liability for that part of the work undertaken by the original contractor.

9.15   Deciding on which of the options would best serve the interests of all the parties is a matter for the employer, perhaps advised by the contract administrator, and the insolvency practitioner. There might be a straightforward way out, or there might be advantages in taking a more pragmatic approach. For example it may prove expeditious to continue initially with the original contractor under some interim arrangement until such time as novation can be arranged, or a completion contract negotiated.

9.16   Following termination, the employer may employ others to complete the work and may use any temporary buildings, equipment, etc on the site for that purpose (cl 6·7·1). The normal payment provisions cease to apply including the requirement to release any retention held (cl 6·7·2). Once the Works have been completed, an account is prepared of the cost of completing the work, and the loss and/or expense and damages suffered as a result of the termination, offset against the amount that would have been paid under the contract (cl 6·7·3). The account is included in a certificate of the contract administrator, or statement of the employer, and the balance claimed from the contractor as a debt, or paid to the contractor as appropriate (cl 6·7·4).

Termination by the contractor

9.17   The contractor is also given the right to determine its own employment if the employer makes default in not paying amounts due (cl 6·8·1·1), or attempts to interfere with or obstruct the issue of any certificate (cl 6·8·1·2), or fails to comply with the requirements of the CDM Regulations (cl 6·8·1·3). It should be noted that despite the wording of clause 6·8·1, which recognises 'any one or more' defaults, a single instance of late payment is unlikely to warrant termination since the contract contains a right of suspension. In addition, termination may be initiated if the Works are suspended for a period of one month or more as a result of a contract administrator's instruction correcting an inconsistency or requiring a variation (cl 6·8·2·1), or because of a default or impediment by the employer (cl 6·8·2·2). If the employer suspends the work this default must affect the whole or 'substantially whole' of the Works for a continuous period of a month or more. In the event of the employer's insolvency, there is an option to terminate, but this is not automatic (cl 6·9). The contract expressly states that the clause 6·8 and 6·9 provisions for termination by the contractor do not prevent the exercise of other rights and remedies which it may possess.

9.18   In the event of a clause 6·8 default, if the contractor wishes to terminate its employment it must first issue a notice which must specify the default complained of and require it to be ended. This is a warning notice to be sent to the employer, and the service of the notice must be in accordance with clause 6·2. If the default is not ended within seven days of the receipt of the notice, the contractor may then by further notice, or within ten days from the expiry of that seven-day period, determine its own employment. Termination then takes effect on the date of receipt of the notice. It appears that if termination did not result and the contractor was to repeat defaults at some later time, then it might be necessary to go through the whole procedure of notices again.

9.19   Upon termination the contractor prepares an account setting out the total value of the work at the date of termination, plus other costs relating to the termination as set out in clause 6·11·2. These may include such items as the cost of removal and any direct loss and/or expense consequent upon termination. The contractor is in effect indemnified against any damages that may be caused as a result of the termination. This would not necessarily be the case if the contractor did not comply with the contractual provisions; in that case it might constitute repudiation. This account is then submitted to the employer, and the employer must pay the amount properly due within 28 days of its submission (cl 6·11·5).

Termination by either party

9.20   Either party is entitled to initiate termination if the works are suspended for a continuous period of one month or more due to various 'neutral' events as set out in clause 6·10·1. If a party wishes to implement this provision, it must issue a notice to that effect. If the suspension does not cease within a further seven days, then that party may issue a second notice terminating the contractor's employment (cl 6·11·1). One of the listed 'neutral' events is loss or damage caused by a Specified Peril, and for this event the contract states that the contractor may not issue a notice where the damage has been caused by its negligence or the negligence of a person for whom it is responsible. Upon termination under clause 6·10, the provisions of clause 6·11 apply as described above, except that amounts of loss and/or damage caused to the contractor are not to be included in the statement of account. In effect the contractor bears the risk of such losses in the event of termination due to neutral events.

10 Dispute resolution

10.1   If any disputes arise in respect of MW05, the form lists mediation, adjudication, arbitration or legal proceedings as the means by which they may be determined. The parties are required to decide in advance which of the processes will be used and make relevant deletions to the Articles. It is important for the contract administrator to understand the options and to be able to give appropriate advice.

10.2   Article 6 states the right of each party to refer 'any dispute or difference' to adjudication. This right comes of course from the Housing Grants, Construction and Regeneration Act 1996, which applies to all 'construction contracts'. MW05, however, may well be used in situations which come within the exception set out in section 106 of the Act, where it states that the Act does not apply to a 'construction contract' with a residential occupier. In such cases there will be no statutory right to adjudication but, unless the parties indicate otherwise, adjudication will still be a contractual right. The wording of the contract would have to be amended if this is not to apply. The parties should give consideration to the relative merits of adjudication, arbitration and litigation, in particular whether they wish an immediate albeit 'temporary' solution, or whether they would prefer a final decision, such as that which would be provided by short form arbitration. In any event the form should never be amended unless the parties are quite certain that the Act does not apply to their contract.

10.3   Where Article 7 applies, final determination of any dispute or difference will be by means of arbitration, and this will be in accordance with Schedule 1 and the JCT 2005 edition of the Construction Industry Arbitration Rules (CIMAR). If the parties reject arbitration, this must be indicated in the Contract Particulars, otherwise the dispute will be resolved by litigation, then Article 7 will be deleted and Article 8 becomes operative. It is important that the architect explains the implications of arbitration and, if the employer is a consumer, the possible effects of the Unfair Terms In Consumer Contracts Regulations 1994. It should be noted that the arbitration agreement may be considered 'unfair' with respect to those Regulations in so far as it relates to disputes involving small sums, as provided by section 91 of the Arbitration Act 1996. Before advising on this decision, the architect should also establish whether the employer is likely to be eligible for Legal Aid. If Legal Aid is a possibility, then it would undoubtedly be better to select litigation.

Alternative dispute resolution

10.4   Negotiations, or adopting some voluntary method of agreement, might be a better initial approach before formal procedures are invoked, but the architect should tread carefully before becoming involved. Advising the client and providing information might be of great help, but the architect will usually have no authority to negotiate terms or agree to contract amendments. Even if authority is given to negotiate a settlement, the architect should take care not to be drawn into complex areas of law which might be better left to a lawyer to handle.

10.5   MW05 includes mediation under clause 7·1, whereby the parties may agree … to resolve their disputes by means of mediation. JCT Practice Note 28 'Mediation on a Building or Sub-contract Dispute' explains the procedures that may be used in appointing a mediator, and what form the outcome might take. It need not result in a binding agreement, of course.

10.6   Nevertheless, there can be many advantages to mediation. Unlike adjudication, arbitration or litigation, it is a non-adversarial process which tends to forge good relationships between the parties. Imposed solutions may leave at least one of the parties dissatisfied and may make it very difficult to work together in the future. If the parties are keen to promote a long-term business relationship they should give mediation serious consideration. Even if mediation does not result in a complete solution, it has been found in practice that it can help to clear the air on some of the issues involved and establishes common ground. This, in turn, might then pave the way for shorter and possibly less acrimonious arbitration or litigation.

Adjudication

10.7   The Housing Grants, Construction and Regeneration Act 1996 (HGCRA 1996) requires that parties to the construction contracts falling within the definition set out in the Act have the right to refer any dispute to a process of adjudication which complies with requirements stipulated in the Act. Article 6 of SBC re-states this right, and refers to clause 7·2, which states that where a party decides to exercise this right 'the Scheme shall apply'. This is referring to the Scheme for Construction Contracts, a piece of secondary legislation which sets out a procedure for the appointment of the adjudicator and the conduct of the adjudication. The Scheme takes effect as implied terms in a contract, if and to the extent that the parties have failed to agree on a procedure that complies with the Act.

10.8   By stating 'the Scheme shall apply', MW05 is effectively annexing the provisions of the Scheme to the form, which therefore become a binding part of the agreement between the parties. Clause 7·2 allows for the parties to determine how the adjudicator will be appointed, by means of appropriate insertions in the Contract Particulars. Under MW05 the adjudicator may either be named in the Particulars, or nominated by the nominating body identified in the Contract Particulars.

10.9   The party wishing to refer a dispute to adjudication must first give notice under section 1(1) of the Scheme (see Figure 12). The notice should identify briefly the dispute or difference, give details of where and when it has arisen, set out the nature of the redress sought, and include the names and addresses of the parties, including any specified for the giving of notices (s.1(2)). If the adjudicator is named in the contract, he or she will normally have already signed terms of appointment on the JCT Adjudication Agreement for a Named Adjudicator (Adj/N). If no adjudicator is named, the parties may either agree an adjudicator or either party may apply to the 'nominator' identified in the Contract Particulars (s.2(1)). If no nominator has been selected, then the contract states that the referring party may apply to any of the nominators listed in the Contract Particulars. The adjudicator will then send terms of appointment to the parties. In addition to the form for a named adjudicator, the JCT also publishes an adjudication agreement (Adj) for use in this situation.

Figure 12 Appointment under the JCT provisions

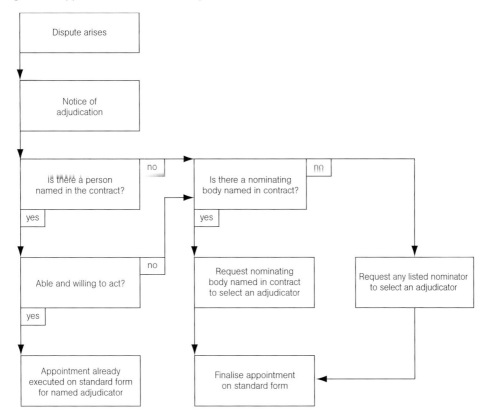

10.10   The Scheme does not stipulate any qualifications in order to be an adjudicator but does state that the adjudicator 'should be a natural person acting in his personal capacity' and should not be an employee of either of the parties (s.4). If the adjudicator is to be named, the subject matter of the dispute will not be known at that time, so it would be sensible to name an adjudicator with a broad range of experience. If the nominating body route is used, that body will normally select an adjudicator with suitable experience from its panel. Where the person does not have the appropriate expertise, he or she must appoint an independent expert to advise and report. The adjudicator is required to act impartially, and to avoid unnecessary expense (s.12).

10.11   The referring party must refer the dispute to the selected adjudicator within seven days of the date of the notice (s.7(1)).

10.12   The referral will normally include particulars of the dispute, a summary of the contentions on which the referring party relies, a statement of relief or remedy sought, and any material it wishes the adjudicator to consider, and must include a copy of, or relevant extracts from, the contract (s.7(2)). A copy of the referral must be sent to the other party (s.7(3)). The adjudicator must confirm receipt of referral documents.

10.13   The adjudicator will then set out the procedure to be followed. A preliminary meeting may be held to discuss this; otherwise the adjudicator may send the procedure and timetable to both parties. The party who did not initiate the adjudication (the responding party) is required to respond within seven days of the date of referral. The adjudicator is likely to hold a short hearing of a few days at which the parties can put forward further arguments and evidence. There may also be a site visit. Occasionally it may be possible to do the whole thing by correspondence (often termed 'documents only').

10.14   The adjudicator is given considerable powers under the Scheme, including the right to take the initiative in obtaining the facts and the law, the right to issue directions, the right to revise decisions and certificates of the architect, the right carry out tests (subject to obtaining necessary consents), and the right to obtain from others necessary information and advice. The adjudicator must give advance notice if intending to take legal or technical advice.

10.15   The Act requires that the decision is reached within 28 days of referral, but it does not state how this date is to be established (s.108(2)(c)). Under the Scheme the 28 days starts to run from the date of the referral notice, which may be earlier than the receipt of all the information by the adjudicator (s.19(1)). The period can be extended by up to 14 days by the referring party, and further by agreement between the parties. The decision must be delivered forthwith to the parties, and the adjudicator may not retain it pending payment of the fee. The provisions state that the adjudicator must give reasons for the decision if requested to do so by the parties (s.22).

10.16   The parties must meet their own costs of the adjudication, unless they have agreed that the adjudicator shall have the power to award costs. The adjudicator is entitled to charge fees, and expenses that are 'reasonably incurred'. The adjudicator is entitled to apportion these between the parties, but if not the parties will bear these in equal proportions. The parties are liable jointly and severally for the adjudicator's fees and expenses, which means that in the event of default by one party, the other party becomes liable for the full amount.

10.17   The adjudicator's decision will be final and binding on the parties 'until the dispute or difference is finally determined by legal proceedings, by arbitration, or by agreement between the parties'. The effect of this is that if either party is dissatisfied with the decision, it may raise the dispute again in arbitration or litigation, or negotiate a fresh agreement with the other party. If the dispute is raised again in a further tribunal, the dispute would be considered again from scratch, with new evidence if necessary, and would not be in the form of an appeal from the adjudicator's decision. In all cases, however, the parties remain bound by the decision and must comply with it until the final outcome is determined.

10.18   If either party refuses to comply with the decision, the other may seek to enforce it through the courts. Generally actions regarding adjudicators' decisions have been dealt with promptly by the courts and the recalcitrant party has been required to comply.

Arbitration

10.19   Arbitration refers to proceedings in which the arbitrator has power derived from a written agreement between the parties to a contract, and which is subject to the provisions of the Arbitration Act 1996. Arbitration awards are enforceable at law. An arbitrator's award can be subject to appeal on limited grounds.

10.20   If arbitration is selected as the method for final determination of disputes, then this is confirmed by deleting Article 8. The arbitration provisions are referred to in clause 7·3 and set out in Schedule 1: Arbitration, which refers to the Construction Industry Model Arbitration Rules (the Rules). The Arbitration Act 1996 confers wide powers on the arbitrator unless the parties have agreed otherwise, but leaves detailed procedural matters to be agreed between the parties or, if not so agreed, to be decided by the arbitrator. To avoid problems arising, it is advisable to agree as much as possible of the procedural matters in advance, and MW05 does this by incorporating the Rules, which are very clearly written and self-explanatory. The specific edition referred to is the 2005 Edition published by the JCT (Article 7), which amends some of the Rules and incorporates supplementary and advisory procedures.

10.21   The party wishing to refer the dispute to arbitration must give notice as required by MW05 Schedule 1 paragraph 2.1 and Rule 2.1, identifying briefly the dispute and requiring the other party to agree to the appointment of an arbitrator. If the parties fail to agree within 14 days, either party may apply to the 'appointor', selected in advance from a list of organisations set out in Article 7. If no appointor is selected, then the contract states that the referring party may apply to any listed nominating body.

10.22   The arbitrator has the right and the duty to decide all procedural matters, subject to the parties' right to agree any matter (Rule 5.1). Within 14 days of appointment the parties must each send the arbitrator and each other a note indicating the nature of the dispute and amounts in issue, the estimated length for the hearing and the procedures to be followed (Rule 6.2, as amended). The arbitrator must hold a preliminary meeting within 21 days of appointment to discuss these matters (Rule 6.3 as amended). The first decision to make is whether Rule 7 (short hearing), Rule 8 (documents only) or Rule 9 (full procedure) is to apply. The decision will depend on the scale and type of dispute.

10.23   Under all three Rules, the parties exchange statements of claim and of defence, together with copies of documents and witness statements on which they intend to rely. Under Rule 8 the arbitrator makes an award based on documentary evidence only. Under Rule 9 the arbitrator will hold a hearing at which the parties or their representatives can put forward further arguments and evidence. There may also be a site visit. The JCT amendments set out time limits for these procedures.

10.24   Under Rule 7 (as amended) a hearing is to be held within 21 days of the date when Rule 7 becomes applicable, and the parties must exchange documents not later than seven days prior to the hearing. The hearing should be not more than one day. The arbitrator publishes the award within one month of the hearing. The parties bear their own costs.

10.25   The arbitrator is given a wide range of powers under Rule 4, including the power to obtain advice (Rule 4.21), the powers set out in section 38 of the Arbitration Act 1996 (Rule 4.31), the power to order the preservation of work, goods and materials even though they are a part of work that is continuing (Rule 4.41), the power to request the parties to carry out tests (Rule 4.51), and the power to award costs. Under Schedule 1 paragraph 3 of MW05 the arbitrator is also given wide powers to review and revise any certificate, opinion, decision, requirement or notice and to disregard them if need be, where seeking to determine all matters in dispute.

10.26   Where the arbitrator has the power to award costs, this will normally be done on a judicial basis, i.e. the loser will pay the winner's costs (Rule 13.1). The arbitrator will be entitled to charge fees and expenses and will apportion those fees between the parties on the same basis. The parties are jointly and severally liable to the arbitrator for fees and expenses incurred.

Litigation

10.27   Where the parties have rejected arbitration and deleted Article 7, then Article 8 becomes operative and disputes will be determined by legal proceedings.

10.28   Litigation cases involving claims for amounts greater than £25,000 are normally heard in the High Court, and construction cases are usually heard in the Technology and Construction Court, a specialist department of the High Court which deals with technical or scientific cases. Procedures in court follow the Rules of the Supreme Court, with the timetable and other detailed arrangements being determined by the court. A judge will hear the case, and in the High Court a barrister must represent the parties.

10.29   Disputes in building contracts have traditionally been settled by arbitration. Arbitrators are usually senior and experienced members of one of the construction professions, and for many years it was felt that they had a greater understanding of construction projects and the disputes that arise than might be found in the courts. These days, however, the judges of the Technology and Construction Court have extensive experience of technical construction disputes. The high standards now evident in these courts are likely to be matched in practice by only a few arbitrators.

10.30   The court has powers to order that actions regarding related matters are joined (for example where disputes between an employer and contractor, and contractor and sub-contractor, concern the same issues). This is much more difficult to achieve in arbitration. Even if all parties have agreed to the CIMAR Rules, the appointing bodies must have been alerted and agreed to appoint the same arbitrator (Rules 2.6 and 2.7). If the same arbitrator is appointed, he or she may order concurrent hearings (Rule 3.73, but may only order consolidated proceedings with all the parties' consent (Rule 3.9), which is often difficult to obtain. The court's powers may therefore be an advantage in multi-party disputes, to avoid duplication of hearings and possible conflicting outcomes.

10.31 There remain, however, two key advantages to using arbitration (see *Lupton*, 1997). The first is that in arbitration the proceedings can be kept private – this is something which is usually of paramount importance to construction professionals and companies, and is often a deciding factor in selecting arbitration. In court, the proceedings are open to the public and the press, and the judgement is published and widely available.

10.32 The second advantage to the parties is that the arbitration process is consensual. The parties are free to agree on timing, place, representation and the individual arbitrator. This autonomy carries with it the benefits of increased convenience, and possibly savings in time and expense. The parties avoid long waiting lists currently running at the High Court, and choose a convenient time and place for the hearing. In arbitration, however, the parties have to pay the arbitrator and for the cost of renting premises in which the hearing is held.

10.33 Where parties have selected arbitration under Article 7, it is still open for them to elect litigation once a dispute develops. If, however, one party commences court proceedings, the other may ask the court to stay the proceedings on the grounds that an arbitration agreement already exists. This would not apply to litigation to enforce an adjudicator's decision, as Article 7 excludes all disputes regarding the enforcement of a decision of an adjudicator from the jurisdiction of the arbitrator.

Appendix A: *Clause comparison table: Destinations*

Table of destinations

	MW 98 (1-4)	MW05	MWD05	subject	changes
Recitals	first	first	first	work, contract documents	split into two recitals
	first	second	third	work, contract documents	
			second	contractor's designed portion	new
	second	third	fourth	priced document	re-worded
	third	second	third	contract documents	become part of second recital
	fourth			quantity surveyor	omitted, now covered by Article 4
		fourth	fifth	CIS	new, introduced by amendment 1
	fifth	fifth	sixth	CDM	re-worded
Articles	Article 1	Article 1	Article 1	contractor's obligations	wording (definition of terms) clarified
	Article 2	Article 2	Article 2	Contract Sum	minor changes
	Article 3	Article 3	Article 3	architect/contract administrator	minor changes
	Article 4	Article 4	Article 4	planning supervisor	re-worded, under amendment 1 now the CDM co-ordinator
	Article 5	Article 5	Article 5	principal contractor	minor changes
	Article 6	Article 6	Article 6	adjudication	Scheme for Construction Contracts now applies. Article simplified and refers to clause 7·2 (List of chairman in Contract Particulars 7·2)
	Article 7A	Article 7	Article 7	arbitration	Default changed to litigation. Exceptions included: Disputes arising under the CIS or VAT-legislation provides another method/any disputes of any decision of an adjudicator
	Article 7B	Article 8	Article 8	legal proceedings	re-worded
	Article 7C			fallback position	omitted

Table of destinations Continued

Articles	MW 98 (1-4)	MW05	MWD05	subject	changes
Definition and Interpretation (new to MW05)					
		1·1	1·1	Definitions	new
		1·2	1·2	Agreement to be read as a whole	new, imports text from 3·6
		1·3	1·3	Heading, references to persons, legislation	new
Clauses					
	Intention of the parties				
	1·1	2·1·1	2·1	contractor's obligations	Re-structured, reference to due diligence omitted, reference to CSCS and contractor design added
	1·1	2·1·2	2·2·1	contractor's obligations	Re-structured, reference to CSCS and contractor design added
		2·1·3	2·2·2	CSCS	new
			2·1·1	complete design	new
			2·1·2	not be responsible for employer's requirements	new
			2·1·3	comply with directions to integrate design	new
			2·1·4	comply with CDM	new
			2·1·5	provide drawings	new
			2·1·6	not commence work until 7 days have elapsed	new
	1·2	2·3	2·4	Architect's duties	unchanged
	1·3	3·10	3·10	Reappointment of Planning Supervisor	re-worded
	1·4	3·9·2	3·9·2	Notification by C	omitted
	1·5	1·6	1·6	Service of notices	minor changes
	1·6·1	1·4	1·4	Period of days	minor changes
	1·6·2	1·1	1·1	Definitions: Public Holiday	minor changes
	1·7	1·7	1·7	Applicable law	minor changes
	1·8	1·5	1·5	Right of 3rd parties	minor changes

Table of destinations Continued

Clauses	MW 98 (1-4)	MW05	MWD05	subject	changes
	Commencement and completion				
	2·1	2·2	2·3	Commencement and completion	minor changes
	2·2	2·7	2·8	Extension of contract period	unchanged
	2·0	2·8·1	2·9·1	Damages for non-completion	minor changes
	2·3	2·8·2	2·9·2		minor changes
	2·3	2·8·3	2·9·3		minor changes
	2·4	2·9	2·10	Practical Completion	unchanged
	2·5	2·10	2·11	Defects Liability	reference to frost damage omitted, clause restructured: Period refers to 'Rectification period' which is stated in Contract Particulars/Suggestion of 3 months
	Control of works				
	3·1	3·1	3·1	Assignment	minor changes
	3·2·1	3·3·1	3·3·1	sub-letting	clarified that the C remains responsible for the compliance with the C documents, H&S Plan and Statutory Requirements (as clause 2·1)
	3·2·2	3·3·2	3·3·2	sub-letting	re-worded
	3·2·2	3·3·3	3·3·3	sub-letting	New: sub-C's employment shall terminate when C's employment terminates (for any reason)
	3·3	3·2	3·2	Contractor's representative	title changed to 'Person-in-charge', otherwise unchanged
	3·4	3·8	3·8	Exclusions from the works	unchanged
	3·5	3·4	3·4	Architect's instruction	forthwith carry out' replaced by 'forthwith comply', therefore clear includes instructions that do not require a positive act
	3·5	3·5	3·5	non-compliance with instruction	re-worded; E may instruct 'any work whatsoever as may be necessary' but may only recover 'additional cost incurred in giving effect to the instruction', not 'all cost'
	3·6	1·2	1·2	priority of printed terms	agreement to be read as a whole' added

Table of destinations Continued

Clauses	MW 98 (1-4)	MW05	MWD05	subject	changes
	3·6	2·4	2·5	Correction of inconsistencies	unchanged
	3·7	3·6·1	3·6·1	Variations	minor changes
	3·7	3·6·2	3·6·2	Variations	Largely new: CA and C to endeavour to agree a price
	3·7	3·6·3	3·6·3	Variations	minor changes
	3·8	3·7	3·7	Provisional sum	unchanged
	Payment				
		4·1	4·1	VAT	
	4·1	4·2	4·2	Payments subject to Supplemental Condition C	Direct reference to 'Construction Industry Scheme' (CIS), supplemental Condition removed
	4·2·1	4·3/4·3·1	4·3/4·3·1	Progress payments and retention	unchanged
	4·2·1	4·3·2	4·3·2	Progress payments and retention	unchanged
	4·2·2	4·4	4·4	failure to pay amount due	minor changes
	4·3	4·5	4·5	Penultimate Certificate	minor changes
	4·4·1	4·6·1	4·6·1	Notices of amounts to be paid + deductions	requirement to state to what amount relates and basis of calculation
	4·4·2	4·6·2	4·6·2	Notices of amounts to be paid + deductions	re-worded
	4·4·3	4·6·3	4·6·3	Notices of amounts to be paid + deductions	re-worded
	4·5·1·1	4·8·1	4·8·1	Final Certificate	unchanged
	4·5·1·2	4·8·2	4·8·2	Final Certificate	requirement to state to what amount relates and basis of calculation
	4·5·1·3	4·8·3	4·8·3	Final Certificate	unchanged
	4·5·1·4	4·8·4	4·8·4	Final Certificate	re-worded
	4·5·2	4·9	4·9	Final Certificate	now combined as general right to interest
	4·6	4·11	4·11	Contribution, levy and tax changes	unchanged
	4·7	4·10	4·10	Fixed price	unchanged
	4·8	4·7	4·7	Rights of suspension by a contractor	unchanged

Table of destinations Continued

Clauses	MW 98 (1-4)	MW05	MWD05	subject	changes
	Statutory obligations				
	5·1	2·1·1	2·1·1	statutory obligations, notices, fees and charges	re-worded
	5·1	2·5·1	2·5·1	Divergences from Statutory Requirements	minor changes
	5·1	2·5·2	2·5·2	Divergences from Statutory Requirements	minor changes
	5·1	2·6	2·6	fees and charges	minor changes
	5·2	4·1	4·1	Value added tax	re-worded
	5·3	4·2	4·2	Construction Industry Scheme	Direct reference to 'Construction Industry Scheme' (CIS), supplemental Condition removed
	5·5	6·6	6·6	Prevention of corruption	minor changes
	5·6	3·9	3·9	Employer's obligation (CDM)	re-worded
	5·6	3·9·1	3·9·1	Employer's obligation (CDM)	re-worded
	5·7	3·9·2	3·9·2	Duty of principal contractor	re-worded
	5·8	3·10	3·10	Successor appointed as principal Contractor	minor changes
	5·9	3·9·3	3·9·3	Health and Safety file	re-worded
	Injury, damage and insurance				
	6·1	5·1	5·1	Injury to or death of persons	Wording simplified + 'C+SC taken out and maintain insurance and comply with the relevant legislation' moved to 5·3
	6·1	5·3	5·3	Injury to or death of persons	re-worded
	6·2	5·2	5·2	Injury or damage to property	Wording simplified + 'maintain insurance under the terms of this agreement and specified sum for liability' moved to 5·3
	6·2	5·3	5·3	Injury or damage to property	re-worded
	6·1/6·2	5·3·1	5·3·1		re-worded
	6·1/6·2	5·3·2	5·3·2		re-worded
	6·3A	5·4A	5·4A	Insurance of the works by contractor	re-worded, C to authorise all monies paid to E

Table of destinations Continued

Clauses	MW 98 (1-4)	MW05	MWD05	subject	changes
	6·3B	5·4B	5·4B	Insurance of works and existing structure by employer	re-worded
		5·4C	5·4C	Insurance of existing structure by employer	new, amendment 1
	6·4	5·5	5·5	Evidence of Insurance	re-worded, no requirement on E to produce evidence of insurance of the works if a Local Authority
Determination					
	7·1	6·2	6·2	Notices	re-worded
	7·2·1	6·2	6·2	Notices	re-worded
	7·2·1	6·4	6·4	determination by the employer – default	minor changes
	7·2·2	6·1	6·1	definition insolvency	definition clarified
	7·2·2	6·2	6·2	Notices	re-worded
	7·2·2	6·5	6·5	determination by the employer – insolvency	minor changes
	7·2·3	6·7·1	6·7·1	following determination by employer	reworded: E may take possession of site and materials
	7·2·3	6·7·2	6·7·2	obligation to make further payment	re-worded
		6·7·3	6·7·3	payment following determination	new obligation on E to prepare an account
		6·7·4	6·7·4	payment following determination	preparation of account
	7·2·4	6·3·1	6·3·1	without prejudice	minor changes
		6·3·2	6·3·2	reinstatement of employment	New: Agreement between the parties
	7·3·1	6·2	6·2	Notices	re-worded
	7·3·1	6·8·1	6·8·1	determination by the contractor – default	minor changes
	7·3·1·3	6·8·2	6·8·2	determination by the contractor – default	re-worded, now broader as suspension due to CAs instruction or 'any impediment, prevention or default by the E/A or E's responsible person no grounds for termination'
	7·3·2	6·1	6·1	definition insolvency	definition clarified
	7·3·2	6·2	6·2	Notices	re-worded

Table of destinations Continued

Clauses	MW 98 (1-4)	MW05	MWD05	subject	changes
	7·3·2	6·9·1	6·9·1	Insolvency of employer	Reworded: Cs obligation to continue the works ceases immediately after the E becomes Insolvent
		6·10	6·10	termination by either party	New provision: Termination by either Party by event in the event work suspended for one month for stated reasons
	7·3·3	6·11	6·11	consequences of termination	reworded, with additional provisions as below
		6·11·2·2	6·11·2·2	consequences of termination	C entitled to be paid for materials and good it is legally bound to pay for
		6·11·4	6·11·4	consequences of termination	clarifies payment to be 'without deduction of any retention' and that materials paid by E to become his property
	7·3·4	6·3·1	6·3·1	without prejudice	minor changes
	Settlement and disputes				
	footnote (v)	7·1	7·1	Mediation	new clause replaces footnote
	8·1	7·2	7·2	Adjudication	JCT adjudication rules replaced by the Scheme
	8·2	7·3	7·3	Arbitration	minor changes
	8·3			Legal proceedings	
	Supplemental Conditions				
	A	Schedule 2	Schedule 2	Contribution, levy and tax changes	reworded: changes as follows: the C is required to incorporate terms into sub-contracts (Schedule 2:3); sums allowable to be added to contract sum (Schedule 2:6); C to provide evidence (Schedule 2: 7); base date to be defined (Schedule 2:12·1); new definition (Schedule 2:12·5); percentage addition deleted (Schedule 2:13)
	B	1·1	1·1	Value added tax	VAT agreement replaced by single clause
	C	4·2	4·2	Construction Industry Scheme (CIS)	provisions replaced by single clause
	D	7·2	7·2	Adjudication	Scheme to apply
	E	Schedule 1	Schedule 1	Arbitration	minor changes

Appendix B: *Clause comparison table: Origins*

Table of origins

	MW05	MWD05	MW 98 (1-4)
Recitals	first	first	first
	second	third	first, third
	third	fourth	second
	fourth	fifth	
	fifth	sixth	fifth
Articles	Article 1	Article 1	Article 1
	Article 2	Article 2	Article 2
	Article 3	Article 3	Article 3
	Article 4	Article 4	Article 4
	Article 5	Article 5	Article 5
	Article 6	Article 6	Article 6
	Article 7	Article 7	Article 7A
	Article 8	Article 8	Article 7B
Clauses	Section 1: definitions and interpretation		
	1·1	1·1	1·6·2 and other clauses
	1·2	1·2	3·6
	1·3	1·3	
	1·4	1·4	1·6·1
	1·5	1·5	1·8
	1·6	1·6	1·5
	1·7	1·7	1·7
	Section 2: carrying out of the works		
	2·1	2·1	1·1, 5·1
	2·2	2·3	2·1
	2·3	2·4	1·2
	2·4	2·5	3·6
	2·5	2·6	5·1
	2·6	2·7	5·1
	2·7	2·8	2·2
	2·8	2·9	2·3
	2·9	2·10	2·4
	2·10	2·11	2·5
	2·11	2·12	2·5
	Section 3: control of the works		
	3·1	3·1	3·1
	3·2	3·2	3·3
	3·3	3·3	3·2

Table of origins Continued

MW05	MWD05	MW 98 (1-4)
3·4	3·4	3·5
3·5	3·5	3·5
3·6	3·6	3·7
3·7	3·7	3·8
3·8	3·8	3·4
3·9	3·9	5·6, 5·7, 5·8
3·10	3·10	5·8
Section 4: payment		
4·1	4·1	5·2
4·2	4·2	4·1, 5·3
4·3	4·3	4·2
4·4	4·4	4·2·2
4·5	4·5	4·3
4·6	4·6	4·4
4·7	4·7	4·8
4·8	4·8	4·5·1
4·9	4·9	4·5·2
4·10	4·10	4·7
4·11	4·11	4·6
Section %: injury, damage and insurance		
5·1	5·1	6·1
5·2	5·2	6·2
5·3	5·3	6·1, 6·2
5·4A	5·4A	6·3A
5·4B	5·4B	6·3B
5·4C	5·4C	
5·5	5·5	6·4
Section 6: termination		
6·1	6·1	7·2·2, 7·3·2
6·2	6·2	7·1, 7·2·1, 7·2·2, 7·3·1, 7·3·2
6·3	6·3	7·2·4, 7·3·4
6·4	6·4	7·2·1
6·5	6·5	7·2·2
6·6	6·6	5·5
6·7	6·7	7·2·3
6·8	6·8	7·3·1
6·9	6·9	7·3·2, 7·3·3
6·10,	6·10,	7·3·3
Section 7: settlement of disputes		
7·1	7·1	footnote (v)
7·2	7·2	8·1
7·3	7·3	8·2
Schedule 1	Schedule 1	Supplemental conditions E
Schedule 2	Schedule 2	Supplemental conditions A

References

Publications

Aeberli P. (2003) *Focus on Construction Contract Formation*, RIBA Publishing, London
Chappell, D. (2006) *The JCT Minor Works Building Contracts 2005*. Blackwell Publishing, Oxford
Furst, S. and Ramsey, V. (eds.) (2006) *Keating on Construction Contracts*, Sweet & Maxwell, London

Cases

Alfred McAlpine Homes North Ltd v Property and Land Contractors Ltd (1995) 76 BLR 59.
Archivent Sales & Developments Ltd v Strathclyde Regional Council (1984) 27 BLR 98 (Court of Session, Outer House)
Balfour Beatty Building Ltd v Chestermont Properties Ltd (1993) 62 BLR 1
BFI Group of Companies Ltd v DCB Integration Systems Ltd [1987] 1 CILL 348
British Telecommunications plc v James Thompson & Sons (Engineers) Ltd (1999) 1 BLR 35 (HL)
Crestar Ltd v Michael John Carr and Joy Carr (1987) 37 BLR 113 (CA)
Crown Estate Commissioners v John Mowlem & Co Ltd (1994) 70 BLR 1 (CA)
Croudace Ltd v The London Borough of Lambeth (1986) 33 BLR 25 (CA)
C. M. Pillings & Co Ltd v Kent Investments Ltd (1985) 30 BLR 80 (CA)
Dawber Williams Roofing Ltd v Humberside County Council (1979) 14 BLR 70
Department of Environment for Northern Ireland v Farrans (Construction) Ltd (1981) 19 BLR 1 (NI)
F. G. Minter Ltd v Welsh Health Technical Services Organisation (1980) 13 BLR 1 (CA)
Gibbs v Tomlinson (1992) 35 ConLR 86
Glenlion Construction Ltd v The Guinness Trust (1987) 39 BLR 89
H. Fairweather & Co Ltd v London Borough of Wandsworth (1987) 39 BLR 106
H. W. Neville (Sunblest) Ltd v William Press & Son Ltd (1981) 20 BLR 78
J. F. Finnegan Ltd v Community Housing Association Ltd (1995) 77 BLR 22 (CA)
Kruger Tissue (Industrial) Ltd v Frank Galliers Ltd (1998) 57 ConLR 1
Leedsford Ltd v The Lord Mayor, Alderman and Citizens of the City of Bradford (1956) 24 BLR 45 (CA)
London Borough of Barking & Dagenham v Stamford Asphalt Co Ltd (1997) 82 BLR 25 (CA)
London Borough of Hounslow v Twickenham Garden Developments (1970) 7 BLR 81
Lubenham Fidelities and Investments Co Ltd v South Pembrokeshire District Council (1986) 33 BLR 39 (CA)
Michael Salliss & Co Ltd v Calil and William F. Newman & Associates (1987) 13 ConLR 69
McGlinn v Waltham Contractors Ltd (2007) 111 ConLR1
Moresk Cleaners Ltd v Thomas Henwood Hicks (1966) 4 BLR 50
Peak Construction (Liverpool) Ltd v McKinney Foundations Ltd (1970) 1 BLR 111 (CA)
Pearce and High Ltd v John P. Baxter and Mrs A. S. Baxter [1999] 1 BLR 101 (CA)
Peak Construction (Liverpool) Ltd v McKinney Foundations Ltd (1970) 1 BLR 111 (CA)
Rotherham MBC v Frank Haslam Milan and M. J. Gleeson (1996) 78 BLR 1
Rupert Morgan Building Services (CCC) Ltd v David Jervis and Hamlet Jervis [2003] EWCA Cir 1583 (CA)
Ruxley Electronics and Construction Ltd v Forsyth (1995) 73 BLR 1 (HL)

Scott Lithgow Ltd v Secretary of State for Defence (1989) 45 BLR 1 (HL)

Sutcliffe v Chippendale & Edmondson (1971) 18 BLR 149

Sutcliffe v Thackrah (1974) 4 BLR 16 (CA)

Temloc Ltd v Errill Properties (1987) 39 BLR 30 (CA)

Terry Pincott v Fur & Textile Care Ltd (1986) 3-CLD-05-14

The National Trust for Places of Historic Interest and Natural Beauty v Haden Young Ltd (1994) 72 BLR 1 (CA)

Townsend v Stone Toms & Partners (1984) 27 BLR 26 (CA)

Viking Grain Storage Ltd v T. H. White and another (1985) 33 BLR 103

Wates Construction (South) Ltd v Bredero Fleet (1993) 63 BLR 128

West Faulkner Associates v London Borough of Newham (1992) 61 BLR 81

Whittal Builders Co Ltd v Chester-le-Street District Council (1987) 40 BLR 82

William Tomkinson & Sons Ltd v Parochial Church Council of St Michael (1990) 6 CLJ 319, 8 CLD-08-05

Clause Index for MW05 *by paragraph number*

Clause Index for MWD05 *by paragraph number*

Subject Index *by paragraph number*